495

D0392399

Man on Earth

Man on Earth

A PRELIMINARY EVALUATION OF THE ECOLOGY OF MAN

by

S P R Charter

Foreword by Aldous Huxley

Contact Editions, Sausalito, California

HM
101
.C52

© 1962 by S P R Charter
Published by Angel Island Publications, Inc.
Library of Congress Catalog Number 62-15385
All rights reserved
Printed in the United States of America
First Edition, 1962

22899

Foreword

by ALDOUS HUXLEY

"FORGIVE THEM, FOR THEY know not what they do." But will there be forgiveness for those who know quite well what they are doing, and how bad it is, but refuse, none the less, to stop? And what about those whose ignorance is real but voluntary, who don't know and know that they don't know, but make no serious effort to acquire knowledge and blithely persist in criminally idiotic courses of action, which they can always excuse, after the disastrous event, by protesting that they really had no idea — and anyhow, everyone else was doing the same thing.

It is the great merit of Charter's book that it compels us to ask such questions — to ask them of our rulers and our elected representatives, of agri-business and industrial businessmen, of technologists and tax-paid research scientists, of the consuming public at large and of ourselves in particular. What are we all doing about the one overriding problem that now confronts the human race — the problem of Man on Earth? As individuals, are we trying to actualize more of our own and our children's desirable potentialities? Or are we content to remain what we are, the less than fully human progenitors of descendants who will probably be even less fully human than ourselves? And as citizens, are we working to create a social and physical environment fit for fully human beings, or an environment incompatible with the full humanity of the individuals condemned to live in it? And finally, as members of Earth's dominant species, are we interested in the survival and, hopefully, the improvement of *Homo sapiens*? Or are we doing our best to accelerate man's extinction or, at the least, his decadence and de-humanization?

At the present time knowledge is in inverse ratio to propinquity, and the financial resources available for scientific research and the translation of theory into practice are directly proportional to a subject's remoteness from life. Thus, we already know a great deal about conditions on the surface of the moon, and are in the process of spending thirty thousand million dollars in order to land a couple of astronauts on that surface. How much do we know about Man on the surface of the Earth? Precious little, considering the importance of the subject. And how much are we prepared to spend on correcting this lamentable ignorance? The answer is the same: precious little. How is man in his demographic, physiological, psychological, and cultural totality related to the totality of his natural and artificial surroundings? This is the question to which Human Ecology attempts to find an answer. For men as enjoying and suffering individuals, men as citizens, and men as members of our planet's dominant and most destructive species, Human Ecology is by far the most important of the sciences. It is also, ironically, the least developed of the sciences, the most nearly non-existent.

The phrase that most frequently recurs in these wide-ranging essays of Charter's is a four-syllabled confession of ignorance: "We do not know."

"Will Earth be able to support its population in another 196 years?" asks the Human Ecologist.

In all honesty he has to answer, "We do not know."

"Our rate of destructive consumption is accelerating. Are we capable of increasing our rate of replacement?"

"We do not know."

"The child born at this moment — what quantities of basic ingredients of our planet will be withdrawn during the 25,000 days of his life? What are these ingredients? How much of them does Earth contain?"

"We do not know."

"What waste products and pollutants will the child expel onto the Earth during his lifetime? What is the inter-relationship of the growing child with the aging Earth?"

"We do not know."

The child needs milk; for "from the time of the first mammals milk in its unaltered form was necessary for survival. . . . In recent years it has become impossible to secure unaltered milk." Is the white stuff, produced by the standardized milk-machines that used to be cows, a more healthful product now than it was a few years ago?

"We do not know."

Cows get penicillin ointment rubbed into their sore udders, and an anti-oxidant is sprayed on their hay. Penicillin and anti-oxidants get into the milk and adversely affect the health of many milk-drinkers. "But far more important," remarks the Human Ecologist, "than penicillin effects or anti-oxidant effects is the total spectrum of inter-relationships of myriad chemical additives permeating our environment. Which additives go through the human digestive tract and which are retained for varying lengths of time, during which they may accelerate varying side-effects?"

"We do not know."

And what about the side-effects of chemical additives upon man's total environment? "Nature can put virulence into pathogens much more rapidly than man can put resistance into crop plants. The chemical industry is continually called upon to develop new additives in man's continuous struggle against nature. Massive doses of additives are applied to crops with primitive discrimination. Wind-drifts carry some of these massive applications over much of the Earth ... with what long-term effects?"

"We do not know."

And now for a special case. "The rich valleys of our country that produce such amazing volumes of crops have generally been in production for less than a hundred years. How long can they remain in their present stage of artificially stimulated fecundity?"

"We do not know."

Swords into ploughshares, atoms for peace — what a laudable ideal! "But at present there are no harmless peaceful uses of atomic energy except as a meticulously controlled tool for further basic atomic research. The authority for this statement is the National Academy of Sciences. What are we to do with the radioactive by-products" of atoms for peace?

"We do not know."

And what about fallout, what about the effects of a slight but long-continued increase in the amount of radiation to which human beings are subjected? Charter answers the question in the words of a report issued in 1960 by the National Academy of Sciences. "The difficulty confronting the scientist is that many of the essential facts necessary to arrive at the answers sought are not yet available, and — what is worse — are not likely to be quickly available."

Yet again, and in a matter of supreme importance to the whole species, "We do not know."

We do not know and we know that we do not know. Nevertheless we continue to pursue courses of action that will, as likely as not, result in irreversibly disastrous consequences for the entire human race. And there are always plenty of experts to condone and justify such courses of action. "Because he is under great pressure for an answer," the 1960 report of the Academy of Sciences continues, "the scientist is forced uneasily into extrapolation or prediction."

"This is unquestionably true," Charter adds, "and unquestionably not the whole truth. Many scientists extrapolate and predict willingly and even anxiously; this is especially true when they seek further public funds for their pet projects."

Money talks, and its talk is one of the "pressures" under which even those who are supposed to be dedicated to the dispassionate contemplation of reality and a scrupulous adherence to the truth may break down. There is a sociology of thought, and even science and philosophy have their vested interests. Outside the laboratory, beyond the ivied walls, money talks more loudly; reason and decency are constantly under enormous economic pressures. For example, everybody knows (there is no question, in this case, of extenuating ignorance) that it is sheer folly to cut down forests without replanting. But more money can be made that way, more quickly. Over vast areas of the Earth the lumber industry is indulging in this kind of insane delinquency. In the name of

free enterprise it is making the world safe for state socialism
or ruin, or a mixture of both. Again, everyone knows that dry
spells alternate with wet spells, and that during rainless
periods in a region of low precipitation grasslands that have
been transformed by the plough into wheatfields are apt to
blow away or be eroded by the first storm. In spite of which,
during every wet cycle and whenever the price of wheat rises,
these marginal grasslands are duly ploughed up. A few people
make a lot of money. Then come the dust storms, the gully-
ing, the sheet erosion. Another inch of the land's nine inches
of fertile topsoil — an inch which it will take the Earth a
thousand years to replace — goes out to sea. Sometimes in
ignorance, sometimes with a full knowledge of what they
were doing, but always under the pressure of a desire for
immediate gain, Americans have, in their short history, irre-
trievably ruined an area of fertile land about twice the size
of the croplands of California, and have nearly ruined the
equivalent of some four of five more Californias.

"After me the deluge" — and, punctually, the deluge ar-
rives. Forethought is incompatible with now-greed.

On the level of collective action, the most dangerous pressures are those exerted by nationalistic, religious, and political ideologies, by the lust for power which animates the ruling
oligarchies who make use of these ideologies for their own and
their society's immediate advantage, and by the bottomless
suggestibility of the masses who believe what they are told,
however nonsensical, and obediently act upon their beliefs.
Almost all our thinking about the human situation is done
with a frame of reference whose coordinates are the grotesque
idée fixes of nationalistic and politico-economic ideologies.
Thinking in these terms, we find it difficult even to pose the
problem of Man on Earth, and we absolutely guarantee ourselves against finding its solution. The intellectual and material resources which ought to be used for insuring man's

survival and improvement are lavished instead on the instruments of mass destruction; and a good slice of what is left over, after the instruments of mass destruction have been bought, goes into the creation of the instruments, electronic and typographic, of mass distraction and mass mis-instruction.

A hundred nations, all sovereign but most of them non-viable, jockey for power and, if they are rich, make themselves richer, if poor, sink into a poverty yet more abject.

Fifty million Americans suffer from the self-induced disease of obesity. Elsewhere two thousand millions of their fellow humans go chronically hungry, seven hundred million adults, to say nothing of their children, remain illiterate and all the time world population is increasing at an annual rate, not of thirty-six millions, as Charter writes in an essay dated from 1960, but (so UNESCO now officially informs us) of more than fifty millions. When Christ was born, world population was about two hundred and fifty millions, and when Shakespeare died, it was about five hundred millions. It had taken sixteen hundred years for human numbers to double. Today there are three thousand millions of human beings on this planet, and by the year 2000, unless something extraordinarily bad or miraculously good should happen in the interval, there will be six thousand millions of us. Twelve times as many people will double their numbers in one-fortieth of the time required for a doubling of population in the fairly recent past. Given these simple demographic facts, what is the probability that we or our children or our children's children will succeed in finding a satisfactory solution to the problem of Man on Earth? It seems pretty safe to answer that, if we go on doing what we are doing now, we shall never find a satisfactory solution.

Modes of thought and courses of action which worked well enough — or at least were not fatal — in the days when it took sixteen hundreds years for two hundred and fifty million human beings to double their numbers are suicidally unsuitable to the human situation today. As a species, we can no longer afford the luxuries of nationalism, power politics, and armaments. We can no longer afford to be governed by officials who believe that problems which appear to be strictly political and economic can be solved by strictly political and economic means. They cannot.

Every political and economic problem requires to be reappraised in the light of Human Ecology, and no solution to a political or economic problem is likely to be complete or lasting unless it takes into account man's biological substratum, together with all the relevant ecological factors in the problem situation. Consider, for example, the case of Africa. Ecologically speaking, the whole continent is in a bad way. The deserts are advancing, the forests are retreating, the soil is being ruined by bad farmers desperately trying to raise more food for an explosively increasing population. What is needed is a continent-wide assessment of available resources, and a continent-wide program of conservation, rehabilitation, and management. But what Africa needs, Africa will not get. Because of the unrealistic terms in which we think of our problems, Africa will get nationalistic rivalries, patchwork economic plans that won't work, increasing poverty for ever larger masses of people living in a steadily deteriorating environment, and, very soon, as the high hopes that accompanied political emancipation prove to be illusory, a general sense of angry frustration, expressing itself in widespread social unrest that will lead inevitably through anarchic disorder to the establishment of competing tyrannies. And what is true of Africa is true, *mutatis mutandis*, of the rest of the world. So long as they continue to think in merely political terms, nationalistic politicians cannot possibly solve the problem of Man on Earth.

On the stage of international politics a whole orchestra of Neros, some consciously malevolent, but most of them full of good intentions and high ideals, insanely fiddle, while all around them, at an ever-accelerating rate, Rome burns. Will the political Neros ever stop their fiddling and do something sensible about the blaze in humanity's far-from-eternal city? Or will they, as politicians have always done in the past, prefer to dull reason and to unexciting forethoughts the thrills of conflict, the allurements of immediate economic advantage, the heady intoxications of power and individual or collective vanity. Yet, once more, we do not know. We can only hope that some of them will read Charter's essays.

(July 20, 1962)

Contents

Man on Earth

*A preliminary evaluation
of the Ecology of Man —*
of the inter-relationship
of man, as a total human
being, with his total
environment.

Introduction

IN THE AUTUMN OF 1960 I began a series of half-hour biweekly
lectures over Pacifica Foundation Radio* under the general
title *Man on Earth*, intended as a preliminary evaluation of
the Ecology of Man — a subject of deep personal concern for
more than a decade. The eighteen essays comprising this
book are taken from the thirty-five broadcasts of this first
series, and bear the dates of their initial broadcast.

Since it is my belief that questions are often more important than answers — that it is the seeds of inquiry which
largely determine the shape of society and the nature of its
aspirations — you may find more questions than answers in

---

*FM stations KPFA (Berkeley, Calif.), KPFK (Los Angeles),
and WBAI (New York) — all solely supported by their listeners'
subscriptions.

this book. They are asked by a scientist not totally bereft of humor and clemency toward himself and his fellow man, in the hope of generating an awareness of the need for a design-theory for man in our age of dilemma.

Science has already furnished us with a plethora of answers to questions, many of which have not even been asked. Most of these answers are not relevant to our survival, much less to our progress upward from the cave. The ambivalent weight of these nonessential answers to nonexistent questions seems to be distorting us into a queer semblance of our human potentiality — and the scream of the lost in the night is unheard and unanswered.

Man, as a total human being, has the capacity to function on all levels of awareness and gradations of promise. While the possession of this capacity does not assure the actual functioning of the individual throughout the entire spectrum of human behavior, the nature of awareness, of itself, does expand his reach until he can embrace his universe. Man's totality is the full measure of his own eternity, directly proportional to individual awareness of himself and his total environment. It is that light which is able, with no diminution of its brilliance, to fire other torches; wherever it strikes the darkness is dispelled.

The irreversible thrust of science into our lives is largely responsible for our numerous dilemmas. Science is not evil; it is good. The men who pursue it, however, have lost to a large extent their love of wisdom and their sense of values; they are leading us astray. The edifice of science may still be sound, but its utility, especially behind those doors closed to enlightened public scrutiny, has become tarnished. While it is not quite the bordello that many accuse it of becoming, it is certainly not the temple it was even a generation ago.

Pursued by those with love of wisdom, searching for man's totality, science can open the grilled gates of uncertainty to vistas of knowledge previously grasped but dimly by minds imprisoned by inexactitude. Already applications of science have extended the individual's days on Earth; broadened, if not deepened, the many bases of his pleasures; and so modified the nature of his response that even in his termination he need know little personal pain. Science has released man from the brutalization of animal-toil and the shackling fears of the unknown, and is making him wealthy beyond the dreams of story-kings.

The grandeur of science is much more, however, than the material abundance emerging from man's applications. It is the majesty of man's mind exposed to the universality of knowledge. The dignity of science has always sprung from the emergence of the individual as he strives to expose the unknown.

Unhappily, the pursuit of science has become enormously costly; and the vast resources it consumes can apparently be supplied mainly by military–industrial complexes. Such complexes inevitably exert their capital powers of expediency; if they did not do so, there would be little reason for the mutually antagonistic existence of so many of them through-out the world — and expediency is conducive to special ad-vantage rather than to universal value. The translation of science into immediate material gain and political power-policy has caused so much of science to become subservient to the military-industrial complexes that the reduction of its universality appears to be unavoidable.

Universality is a principled pursuit; expediency is not. Principles cannot be retained slightly any more than a female can be pregnant only slightly. Is it possible that principles have become a luxury that science can no longer afford if it is to fulfill its promise of abundance so intimately joined to its coexistent threat? While this may be an unpalatable question, the present direction of science indicates that this question should be asked. Accepting its expediency as a matter of need, can science ever return to its universality and historic grandeur? Since the direction science takes is of deep individual concern, these questions are not abstract.

All this is not meant to imply that science is now wholly related to war and is therefore meretricious. Actually, although the threat of total erasure of mankind is present and virulent, only one hand of science is intimately enlaced with international warfare. In many areas unrelated to weaponry, work is being pursued vigorously: in genetics, molecular biology, embryology, immunology, radio astronomy, high-energy nuclear physics, and many others. However, while all science is not related to war, science itself has ceased to be universal for mankind, toward which it has no design-theory for its own endeavors.

Such a design-theory was perhaps not essential for survival when science was a principled pursuit of universal knowledge; but when its present applications and further explorations threaten and are capable of executing the total erasure of mankind, a design-theory toward Man on Earth becomes the immediate and essential ingredient for survival. If no design-theory is evolved the promise of science, which can be enormous, remains shackled to its enormous threat. Even without nations going to war this threat, in actuality, can become terminal for mankind.

The struggle for man's survival seems to be no longer merely between and among nations seeking and possessing mutually destructive weaponry, but to be essentially between man and his constantly altering environment.

It seems quite certain that our continued non-awareness of man's totality will hasten our departure. The Ecology of Man — the inter-relationship of man as a total unsegmented organism with his total uncompartmentalized environment — may be able to evolve a design-theory for the continuation of Man on Earth.

In the expanding spiral of knowledge, the Ecology of Man can be projected from many frames of reference; and the entire world of discourse can be covered from any starting-point: from population pressures, water limitations, the morality of our times, scientific humanism and realism, the inter-relationship of science and the arts of man.

SPRC
April 15, 1962

I

The Growing Child on an Aging Earth

WITH EVERY BEAT OF your heart a child is born onto our planet. Wanted or not; planned for, or the terminal manifestation of prior accident, the child, for the remainder of his life, will consume Earth's resources in a manner and at a rate which we do not yet know and for which we cannot as yet plan.

It has become scientifically fashionable to be concerned with population pressures. Many who worry about the numbers of people on our planet believe that the only workable solution is universal birth control. Others, in opposition, believe that we can copulate ourselves onto a broader economic base by birthing new customers.

Numbers, by themselves, are difficult to relate to reality; time is equally difficult to relate to reality. How many of us can actually feel our personal and genetic history retreating into the haze of 2,000 or 200,000 years past, and advancing into the haze of another 2,000 or 200,000 years hence? To those on Earth in today's Nineteen Sixties is there much personal significance in another 1,960 years?

Yet each of us is a whole human being, a whole number, so to be counted into Earth's present population — as each day and its minutest fraction is a bridge to be crossed from the past into the future. And there is an arithmetic to population increase. When such numbers are related to individuals they are clothed in stark reality.

Man is a relatively new phenomenon on Earth. He has not yet learned to live with his environment, and actually may never do so, but become extinct long before the natural expiration of this planet, to be replaced by an organism that will learn to live with its environment.

A hundred years ago a chemical theory was uncovered that retains broad significance. It is known as the "Law of the Minimum":

> Under ideal circumstances, a reaction will continue until restrained by exhaustion of whatever essential ingredient is present in least supply.

What is our essential ingredient in least supply? And how much of it do we possess?

We do not know.

Quite likely it may emerge that our essential ingredient in least supply is not water, air, land, food, or any other physical item, but our applied intelligence toward the totality of Man on Earth. If this be true, and this most essential ingredient continues in least supply, man may exhaust himself long before the exhaustion of other Earth-resources.

Man's grotesque ignorance of his Ecology is manifest in his anguished attempts to find solutions to over-population. The fact is, we do not know even the extent of the problem.

How could our attempts at solutions be anything but specious, piecemeal, and saddening?

Merely to declare with emphasis and pictorialize with miscellaneous examples that we have too many people is not even stating the preliminary problem of population-pressures confronting the limitations of material resources.

The acre with the greatest population-density is not in India or China but in the center of Manhattan Island. There, some 30,000 people live a good part of their lives on the one-acre Earth-space occupied by the Empire State Building. By extension, if all of New York City's 200,000 acres (315 sq mi) had the same density, six billion people — twice Earth's present population — could there be enclosed.

Why then the cry of overpopulation? Our technology built one Empire State Building. If we built one, can we not build ten? And if ten, why not 10,000 or 200,000 with our new techniques and materials? This is a tentative direction toward solution seriously considered by some advanced planners.

Exponents of vertical living are numerous. Some among them suggest that, as our ground-roads become hardened arteries of slow-flow, we institute uniform building codes so that all roof-tops are built to straight level roadways, with parks and other facilities on top of the buildings. Roads and freespace settings will then be nearer the heavens while the population lives below, in vertical caves. The arithmetic of expansion here finds a mathematical solution — but only for the storage of people.

Can the question of population-increase be recognized from a relatively short-term and a relatively long-term frame of reference?

Although many attempt this approach, neither frame of reference has any relationship to reality or any validity in terms of people.

If we consider as a midway long-term point only the 1,960 years or so between the time of Christ and now — overlooking the further reaches of history into Biblical and pre-Biblical times — in another 1,960 years, under current rates of increase, the physical weight of the population at that time will be more than the weight of the Earth itself. And 1,960 years is not a long span for Nature; many living trees are much older.

Halfway between now and another 1,960 years there will be only one square foot of Earth-space available for every living human being and, even if every acre — every 43,500 sq ft — of Earth had a skyscraper rising from it, each building would have to be half again as high as the Empire State Building merely for the storage of people.

Obviously then, a long-range frame of reference regarding the numbers of people cannot be in terms of time — time here ceases to have a relationship to reality.

Equally obvious — for various reasons, including gravitational mechanics — is the fact that under current rates of increase there can be no population on Earth in another 1,960 years.

What of one-tenth that time? Will Earth be able to support its population in another 196 years?

We do not know.

A short-term frame of reference has no more reality than a long-term frame of reference when we consider that in less than eighteen years the increase of China's population, under present rates, will be greater than the total population of the United States at this moment.

Since such numbers almost defy comprehension, let this example suffice: if every person today in the United States were suddenly to die, at the current rate of world-population-increase the remainder of Earth's inhabitants would replace the loss, in numbers, within five years.

When the Thirteen Colonies united to found a Nation, our country's population was around three million. Today the population increase in our country is approximately three million — every year.

Were annual births not to exceed annual deaths, and world population remained numerically stable at current figures, we would still be hurtling toward material exhaustion at a fixed point in time. Our rate of destructive consumption of basic ingredients — consumption of materials in a manner not permitting re-use — is today greater than our rate of replenishment. Certainly we should determine, as accurately as we can, whether or not we are capable of increasing our rate of replenishment — by how much and how soon.

There was a time when the birth of a child was an occasion for rejoicing. Now, subconsciously or not, we increasingly fear that it is not such an occasion. We have a growing awareness that the only frame of reference for the question of population-increase is the child born this moment, and the child born the next moment, as each will fight the other for survival.

Time, therefore, extended into any sort of future — near or far — has little relationship to reality in terms of the question of population-increase.

Nevertheless, population-increases are a stark reality that can bring about attrition and exhaustion of Man on Earth.

Is the population-question then one of ingredients? Of water, air, food availabilities for increasing numbers of people?

It is scarcely one of ingredients.

The Empire State Building acre receives an average annual rainfall of some 40 inches, which measure just a trifle more than one million gallons of water. The 30,000 people occupying the Empire State Building, along with their attendant facilities, use approximately that much a day. They therefore use a full year's rainfall in one day. The remainder of their annual water needs must come from other unoccupied acres. But the Empire State Building is only for the storage of people.

Can science today devise techniques that will permit the purification and re-use of urine and wash-water over and over again? Yes, without question. We are using such techniques in present manned satellite mock-ups. Of course, much of this country is already consuming water that is filthier than the drinking water in much of Europe, South America, and the Orient. However, we really do know how to purify and re-use water.

Water is without question a definite and limiting factor. Is it, however, our most essential ingredient? We shall probably exhaust ourselves in other ways before we exhaust our water supply, or have it become polluted beyond the point of human use.

Air is, of course, another limiting factor. Each human being is a consumer of energy and a dispenser of waste-materials. A loaf of bread, for example, by the time it reaches the consumer represents a measurable amount of pollutants in our atmosphere — from the exhaust stack of the tractor preparing the land for the planting of the wheat, to the exhaust pipe of the truck delivering the wrapped loaf. Without question science can develop workable techniques that will permit the purification of air. It remains quite possible that air, no longer as pure throughout the world as it was even ten years ago, and becoming increasingly less pure, may become polluted beyond the tolerance for human use.

By then, however, we probably would have exhausted ourselves in other ways.

Food is quite a limiting factor. But masses of people can exist for generations on near-starvation diets. The food-pill prognostication has already made commercial headway in the various near-starvation powders being touted vigorously throughout the land as weight reducers. It is certain that, when this fad has run its course in our country, the powders will be compressed into pills and shipped to areas of immediate need. Over a long period of time such pills may bring about rather startling internal digestive changes; but science can make a food pill. Even without a food pill the United States may, in another fifty years, use emerging techniques to feed one billion people annually, if, by then, we have solved many of the problems of water and air pollution and of erosion and fertile-acre encasement, as well as so many problems of which we have not yet become aware. Then too, by that time this country's population would have doubled, as would the remainder of Earth's population. Can we therefore expect much of a net gain in terms of food?

It is rather doubtful.

At this point in time, all we have are piecemeal answers to piecemeal questions.

The child born at this moment — what quantities of basic ingredients of our planet will he withdraw during the 25,000 days of his life? What are these ingredients? How much of a known supply does Earth possess? We do not know. What do we know, now, about their possible replenishment? What non-material ingredients will the child need during his lifetime? What waste-products and pollutants will the child expel onto his Earth during his lifetime? What is the inter-relationship of the growing child with an aging Earth?

We do not know.

But we can find out.

We possess techniques to gather this knowledge about our Earth; but we do not seem to possess the wisdom to seek it or to recognize its inevitable need.

We cannot truthfully anticipate that science will have solutions before we suffer attrition and exhaustion. Much of the United States suffers at this time from impure water; most of the world's people suffer at this time from actual hunger; all of the world suffers at this time from moral fallout and the threat of total erasure — and for none of these does today's science offer workable solutions.

Most of today's scientists, throughout the world, swear allegiance to governments rather than to the people they help enslave. Their aiding and abetting toward enslavement is not deliberate. It is the near-inevitable effect of the angle of divergence so many scientists accepted in the early days of the nuclear age. Many scientists publish philosophies of science that are mere Apologias; and many more, through their public-relations staffs in universities and research organizations, humanize to the world their nobility of purpose.

Some scientists believe that radioactive fallout may perhaps bring about effective birth control by causing a universal depletion of fecundity, since fallout does have such an effect on reproductive organs. The fact that such fallout is non-discriminatory, that it could affect all on our planet, is cited as a virtue. The fact that such fallout causes irreversible genetic changes is not given much consideration. Actually, birth control may probably be effective through such universal semi-sterilization, but people as human beings will no longer exist. We will be replaced by genetically different organisms.

Several years ago animal-research technicians succeeded in removing the fertilized ovum from a prize Holstein cow and transplanting it in a scrub Jersey cow, where they hoped it would come to term. The purpose of this research was to see whether a prize animal could be used merely for purposes of fertilization, while a scrub animal would be used for the remainder of the gestation period. If the project proved successful, the prize animal could be impregnated eight or ten times a year. Around the same time, a Canadian team of insect-research technicians succeeded in removing the eye area of a fetal insect and replacing it with the eye area of another fetal insect. This insect transplant was successful. The cow transplant was not.

At some point it is quite likely that the cow transplant will become successful; it is equally likely that the insect transplant will have some rather far-reaching implications.

Assuming success in both transplants, strange implications emerge here for man. Suppose we do succeed in genetic transplanting, or in the transplanting of the fertilized ovum into another human carrier within which the ovum completes gestation. Who is the mother of the child?

Suppose we successfully transplant, soon after ovum-fertilization, the head from one ovum, the thorax from another, the extremities from still another? Whom does the child recognize as parent? Which segment-supplier recognizes her child? What race-memories of the species can be expected?

Here, then, without genetic malfunction but only from genetic transplanting, the theoretical problems have already become legion. With genetic malfunction as a normally increasing possibility the problems are infinitely compounded.

Probably the most significant fact regarding population-increase is this:

We will not be able to achieve understanding of the problem — an understanding which is essential before we can hope to develop solutions — unless we first accept the totality of Earth's land, sea, and air as a single undivided planet, and the totality of man as a single undivided human being. In this context there can be no geographic particle-separations or racial separations; these become utterly meaningless.

For example: if all the world's people agreed to have no more than three children in each family, and those late in life so that the subsequent arrival of grandchildren would be delayed, Earth's population would likely remain stable at around three billion. However, should some country with only three million people disagree with this limitation and permit its fecundity free rein, in a matter of some 500 years it would have a population equal to that of the rest of the world.

Quite simply, therefore, any hoped-for solution must have world-wide application.

Similarly, any contemplation of the problem must take into consideration world-wide factors. At this stage, our ignorance of the basic factors relating to the question of overpopulation is unbelievable and unforgivable.

In terms of our available resources we may already have too many people on Earth; we really do not know, because we do not know how many people are on Earth today, and we do not know the extent of this planet's capacity.

We possess proven techniques enabling us to secure such a relatively simple inventory, but we do not use them. We have no such Earth-inventory. The fact that we do not have it, while scientists throughout the world worry over population-pressures, is one indication that we lack applied intelligence toward man's totality.

Even as scientists have segmented mankind into undignified fragments, so have governments segmented our planet into geographic fragments. In terms of population-increases this fragmentation is scientifically unsound. The human reproductive process is certainly not limited to the citizens of any one country.

It is ridiculous merely to state that we have too many people in the world and that unless something is done about it we will have more than too many.

What is the maximum number of people Earth can support today, and at what standard of living? We do not know because we do not know Earth's resources. Even should it be fact that we already have too many people, and that each man's neighbor is his enemy in the continuing struggle for survival, we would not know that.

Groping in the caves gashed out of man's totality by the geographic and scientific fragment-makers, we continue in ignorance.

We do not know the inter-relationship of the growing child with an aging Earth. We do not know, with any sort of accuracy, his subtraction from our planet's resources and his addition to our planet's decay. While we possess proven techniques that would enable us to find out, we must first merge Earth's fragments into one planet. It would avail us little to uncover this information for the child in North America while the child in South America or in the Orient remained shrouded in the haze of unapproachability. Our failure to use our proven skills in this regard is another indication of our lack of applied intelligence toward the totality of man.

Let us assume the possession of a thoroughly effective and uncostly birth-control pill. Which citizens of which country are to be given this pill? At what level should Earth's population be stabilized? At today's? Tomorrow's? Next year's? We do not know. By tomorrow, more than 100,000 people will have been added to this planet. By next year, more than 36 million. The stark reality of such numbers of people cannot be ignored. Which geographic fragment of Earth will hasten to reduce its birthing while all the other fragments continue multiplying?

Birth-control pills are of little avail to a geographically fragmented planet.

Let us assume wisdom and honor among world scientists, and respect their search toward solutions of world population-pressures. One seeks a birth-control pill; another seeks new water sources from the seas and even the stones; a third seeks

increased farm-yields for areas of need; a fourth seeks new
sources of raw materials in remote areas or from new techniques, and so on . . .

From what frame of reference are they functioning? What
are they attempting to solve in terms of population-pressures,
even in terms of their own grandchildren's grandchildren?

Unless we develop a design-theory toward the numbers of
people for our planet and their inter-relationship with it, all
piecemeal search in terms of population-pressure is doomed
to failure.

Only the Ecology of Man can develop this design-theory.

If man, by his own definition, is the highest organism on
Earth, the wildest animal capable of taming all other animals
but himself, then his own fecundity can destroy him; his own
birth rate can asphyxiate him.

Can he control his own fecundity? Only if he applies his
intelligence toward man's totality. What the United Nations
has been unable to accomplish — the unity of nations —
man's birth rate will accomplish by forcing the geographic
fragments into a single planet as our Earth herself struggles
for survival.

One hopes that our progression toward asphyxiation can
be retarded. To give substance to this hope, it is imperative
that we attempt to develop a design-theory toward ourselves
and our planet.

Man is more than a mere chemical cohesion. Even so, the
Law of the Minimum does obtain. Today, our essential ingredient in least supply is our applied intelligence toward
the totality of man. Let us use whatever amounts of this ingredient the world possesses toward building a design-theory
for Man on Earth.

(December 2, 1960)

II

Milk and Moral Fallout

ONCE UPON A TIME, when a man could conceive of his own termination, of his own death, he could, if he wished, take refuge and solace in the beings and things he would leave as his marker of the measure of his days on Earth. He could live with his concept of continuity as a personal stabilizer, and look upon himself and his family as a heritage from the past, through the present, and into the future.

Now, for the first time in history, man can conceive of the total annihilation of his family, his work, and even the memory of his being. He now lives with total erasure as a possibility. This possibility of total erasure casts a shadow upon the value of the individual to himself and his society, and he becomes increasingly a stranger to himself. Probably each of us can see in himself manifestations of such dissipation.

As full of portent to survival as radioactive fallout is the moral fallout enveloping Man on Earth. We have lived for more than fifteen years with this fallout. Many of our younger scientists and technicians have spent all their professional lives in its haze, breathing its putrescence and thinking of it as nectar. All in the world who are fifteen and younger have been born into this decay.

What do we tell these young people of morality and values? What do we tell ourselves? Moral fallout is also cumulative, and its ethical malfunction-probabilities are perhaps equal to the genetic malfunction-probabilities of radioactive fallout. This is one of the hidden yet major prices we have already paid in the consuming and unplanned search for progress which we carry on at accelerated pace, with no design-theory toward the future of Man on Earth.

If science is becoming a meretricious word unworthy of trust, those responsible are reaping a just harvest.

However, to condemn without trying to seek solutions is to surrender without dignity or honor.

Man always modifies his environment and is, in turn, modified by it. This inter-modification is not always upward for his betterment; frequently it is a downward process.

The simplicities of living are gradually and relentlessly disappearing, and all ingredients of living are becoming increasingly complex. In this context it is not a question of what man is; we no longer know what milk is.

Milk is the first sustenance of every mammal; and milk is here used as a first example of the inter-modification of man and his environment. Because milk and its numerous products is universally used throughout the land, its ordinariness may highlight the dramatic nature of inter-modification and moral fallout.

No food technologist, of whatever skill, can now define milk accurately except to say that it is the product of a cow.

A cow is a wandering chunk of Earth. She is still the symbol of man's servitude to the soil and the whimsicalities of weather. The men who tend her are her servants. For her they get up early and go to bed late. If she is sick or in labor her servants crawl out of bed swearing, and wade through her urine and manure to go to her side and help. They have to. In the process of becoming a milk-machine to make profits, the cow has lost, to a large extent, her ability to take care of herself. She has also lost, to an even larger extent, her ability to deliver an unadulterated flow.

From the time of the first mammals on Earth, milk in its unaltered form was necessary for survival. In the past few years it has become almost impossible to secure unaltered milk. Is milk a more healthful product now than it was a few years ago? We do not know with a measurable degree of certainty. Milk has now become suspect as a contributor to disease.

There are many who question the entire animal-fat controversy: how could the product of the cow — used by man for thousands of years — now become harmful? But neither cow nor man are the same as they were thousands of years ago, or even a few years ago. Man today ingests in his normal daily diet many hundreds of ingredients that were not even known several years ago, with little or no present knowledge of the inter-relationships of these ingredients. Man continues to modify himself and his own environment; the modifications may happen quite rapidly and glibly, while knowledge of their implications may be garnered quite slowly. Even then, implications become known only after modifications have become deep-rooted, and very little can be done to reverse the modifications.

The use of soil fertilizers and amendments, feed conditioners and anti-oxidants, pharmaceuticals, pesticides, and insecticides (all here referred to under the general term additives) has been going on with unregulated and indiscriminate intensity for years. Penicillin, a wondrous drug when first introduced, is an excellent example of massive ignorance in this regard.

When a dairy cow suffers from mastitis, an inflammation of one or more milking quarters — a fairly usual ailment every once in a while in most herds — standard practice is to give the affected quarter a dose of penicillin ointment. Even if the cow is not milked for a day or so while waiting for the inflammation to subside, some penicillin residue finds its way into the milk and from there, through processing, onto the consumer's table.

Penicillin-allergy is now recognized as affecting, in some degree, approximately five percent of all people given this drug. Because even the slightest amount of residue can bring on a reaction, it has now become standard practice among allergists to restrict all milk-products whenever penicillin-allergy is suspected.

This, of course, is not a condemnation of penicillin, an extremely useful drug for humans and cows when intelligently applied.

In the summer of 1960, the U.S. Pure Food and Drug Administration, mainly because of this allergy factor, issued an edict that the tolerance for penicillin in consumer-milk would be henceforth 0.0 parts-per-million. We were told, with the weight of government, that penicillin in milk was dangerous for a substantial number of people. Why did it take so long to find out? How effective will such regulation be? The dairyman is held responsible for keeping penicillin-milk out of his bulk tank from which shipments are made to various processing plants; but no dairyman analyzes his milk daily or even weekly. Once a month many dairymen, if they participate in some Dairy Herd Improvement Association program, have a technician analyze the individual cow's milk, but only for butterfat content. At the processing plant milk is normally analyzed for bacterial count and butterfat content upon receipt. Should a shipment of penicillin-milk arrive, the entire bulk-quantity of that tankload, representing the production of several dairy herds, would have to be dumped, and the guilty dairyman held to account. How restive will dairymen and processors become under such restrictions, and what circumventive measures will they seek? Will government feel it has discharged its obligations when it fines a few milk producers who are caught with penicillin-residue?

What of the other, literally hundreds of additives that invade a cow's environment, her milk, and milk-products? Will we again have to wait for a propitious accident to inform us of hazard?

One grocery chain stopped accepting penicillin in milk from its dairymen suppliers two years before the government edict, not because it considered penicillin harmful to humans but because pencillin-residue interfered with its cheese-making processes by inhibiting mold-growth. Must we wait for such accidents before we acquire knowledge? Despite technical progress, milk is a less-known product than it was even a few years ago.

This is not a condemnation of additives, but of our ignorance regarding them and their subtle inter-relationships with our personal environment. It is a condemnation of the drugged panacea-seekers who are altering our total environment almost beyond recognition and recall.

Penicillin is a remarkable tool in knowledgeable hands, but its simplicity of administration has probably retarded medical knowledge to a measurable degree.

In a pocket-community — one that is relatively isolated geographically — where only one physician is available, a penicillin-pusher who uses this one drug as a snake-oil panacea either from greed — because he can charge $5 or more for a quick ten-cent dose — or out of continuing ignorance, can do irrevocable harm. If such a community, with such an unfor-

tunate medical skill, ethics, or conscience, also has dairying
as its major, or only, industry, the combination can be an
invaluable field-laboratory for the study of the inter-relationship of penicillin and milk in cows and humans.

Such a community, actually existing within fifty miles of
San Francisco, has finally come to the attention of research
people interested in this problem.

Once again, this is not a condemnation of milk, but of
our scientific and technical ignorance of this essential food-
ingredient. Milk is here used only as an example of the
inter-relationship of man with his environment. Bread, another rather shaky staff of life these days, could just as well
be used as an example; or water, or air, or any of a number
of Earth-bound simplicities about which our ignorance increases while we search the heavens for more knowledge.

In the mid-Nineteen-Fifties, one of the chemical giants
in this country developed an anti-oxidant which, when used
on harvested alfalfa, would retard Vitamin A losses. Normally good alfalfa — a staple in the feeding of dairy cattle —
would have upon harvest a Vitamin A content of around
200,000 International Units per pound of alfalfa. However,
Vitamin A oxidizes rapidly to the point where its content
could be reduced to 80,000 or 60,000 International Units per
pound of alfalfa within a matter of days. This anti-oxidant,
sprayed onto alfalfa at modest cost, actually helped retain
Vitamin A content at around 120,000 International Units,
which was, of course, a good thing. Except that months later
the Pure Food and Drug Administration declared this anti-
oxidant — even in the residual amounts left in the milk after
the cow had eaten the treated alfalfa — unsuitable for human
consumption. Still later, the Pure Food and Drug Administration changed its collective mind again, and decided its
original ruling was too harsh.

One can conclude, quite justifiably, that they did not know what they were doing.

Even more important than penicillin effects or anti-oxidant effects is the total spectrum of inter-relationships of myriads of additives, in one form or another, permeating our environment with an increasing haze. What is the inter-relationship of a pesticide to an insecticide? And both to a feed-conditioner? And the residual sum of all additives on the individual? No one can escape additives in foods, drinks, and medicines. What are the effects upon the individual of such permutations and combinations? Which additives go through the human digestive tract, and which are retained for varying lengths of time during which they may accelerate varying side-effects?

Nobody knows.

We could try to exert sufficient effort to uncover values and detriments of all these additives. We know atom bombs, think-machines, sputniks, automatic devices for automatic living, but we don't know milk. Only occasionally, and by accident as in the case of penicillin, a globule of knowledge rises to the surface of the morass.

Milk, a simple and age-old ingredient of living, has become infinitely complex, with increasing areas of ignorance. The cud-chewing cow, ruminating in green pastures, has long been a poetic symbol of man's peaceful relationship to the soil. Today her pastures are greened with additives and spattered with varying degrees of radioactive fallout; and even the cow, subjected to our consuming and unplanned search for progress in terms of greater yield, has become the anti-poetic symbol of the moral fallout of man.

No reference is here made to drug manufacturers who issue model changes with a dexterity that shames Detroit; or to physicians who prescribe such drugs knowing virtually nothing about them; or to biochemists who support the families they love by working on genocidal, mass-destruction

chemicals; or to nuclear wastemakers; or to suicidal obso-
lescence-peddlers. This reference is only to a cow.

Are there manifestations of moral fallout even nearer ourselves? Each must answer for himself.

The Ecology of Man can and should be studied from many
frames of reference. For example: many trees, in adding one
pound to their weight, use and discharge into the atmosphere
approximately 35 gallons of clean water. By comparison, a
pound of steel uses some 20 gallons of water in its manufacture; a pound of rayon uses some 180 gallons; a gallon of
ordinary gasoline uses 10 gallons of water, while a gallon of
aviation gasoline uses 25 gallons of water in the refining
process; a steam power plant uses between 600 and 1,000
tons of water for every ton of coal burned. Much of this
industrial water is not re-usable. How many pounds of tree
does a human need in his lifetime, for his body and his spirit?

A cow normally drinks approximately 10 gallons of water
a day, at least three of which become part of the milk she
gives.

Today, in our nation, approximately one-third of the
human population lives with a chronic water shortage, poor
water quality, or a combination of both. This situation cannot be dramatically improved in the near future; it will
probably deteriorate quite drastically. Our government estimates that it would cost $12 billion or more to rid our water-
ways of existing pollution and around $15 billion to keep
them unpolluted.

In the foreseeable future it is doubtful that we will be able
to get immense quantities of clear water from the sea through
the use of nuclear energy as a cheap source of desalting power,
or cheap, inland brackish water-purification through such
energy. We already have problems of nuclear fission waste-
disposal that will be compounded astronomically when nuclear

devices multiply to the point of major economic use. Since most radioactive material eventually finds its way back to Earth and into waterways, the cost of depolluting the cumulative effects of radioactivity from even peaceful uses of nuclear energy, should that become technically possible, would be quite fantastic.

There are some regulations regarding purity of water for human consumption; there are no such regulations regarding purity of water for cows. And the cow herself is not a very efficient water purifier; on the contrary, she creates further purification problems.

What are the effects of various types of water on various additives that are now part of the milk we consume?

Here, again, we plod along in ignorance when answers can be secured.

A few years ago a doctorate thesis was presented at one of our major universities detailing the different kinds of taxes levied against a single egg. Transportation taxes, power taxes, feed, packaging, equipment taxes — each category detailed and documented. It appeared that some 300 different taxes were levied against the egg.

A similar thesis can be presented detailing the different additives and their amounts normally used by an average family in this country during any given day or month. It is safe to assume that the number would stagger belief.

This is not a blanket condemnation of additives, many of which are valuable and needful, but a condemnation of our accepting ignorance regarding their numbers and effects. Admittedly it is a complex problem, but one certainly not beyond solution. Government agencies of all nations should perform this public service, especially as we seem to be placing increasing dependence upon additives.

For example: in 1954 United States agriculture used 1.9 million tons of nitrogen fertilizer; in 1959 this had increased by 40 percent to 2.67 million tons. Phosphates in 1954 were used in agriculture in the amount of 2.2 million tons; in 1959 their use increased by some 12 percent to 2.54 million tons. In 1954 agriculture used 1.8 million tons of potash; by 1959 the increase was almost 20 percent to 2.2 million tons.

These figures are here used only to indicate our increased dependence upon additives. We now know, for example, that too much nitrogen is distinctly harmful in sugar-beet farming, and we now attempt to restrict this additive for this crop as it approaches maturity.

Here, a little globule of knowledge seems to have percolated to the surface.

Additive complications give rise to all sorts of faddism — organic farming, stone-grinding of wheat, and other curiosities. Why some people believe that grinding with stones should make a better flour than grinding with coolant steel is difficult to comprehend. Actually, stone-grinding can leave a granitic or silicon residue in the flour which can be quite harmful. Organic farming, where no manufactured fertilizers or other additives are used, is a near impossibility in our society. Neither can each of us maintain a family cow in a barn-closet.

As available land-supply is engulfed by increasing populations, the cow herself will more than likely disappear and her milk be replaced by a synthetically manufactured substitute. The cow is a poor converter of Earth's resources. Inevitably, the physical space required for her feeding and maintenance will have to be used more economically.

Indications of such a trend presently exist in various parts of the world, especially in the Los Angeles area and around Lima, Peru.

Commercial dairy farming is usually located close to centers of consumer-population. This is so because, even though insulated tank-trucks fill their cargo from the producing ranch's holding-tanks which are normally cooled to 41 degrees Fahrenheit, fluid milk does not hold up very well.

Processing plants are usually located within cities. Because of the dairy herd's proximity to cities, the herd is usually maintained on as few acres as possible, essentially because of land costs. In the Los Angeles area, for example, the average herd numbers 150 cows, and the average acreage for them is 15 acres per herd. This is sometimes called a slab-operation because most of the 15 acres are under concrete for easier herd-handling. In such slab-operations the cow is truly a milk factory, and all her feed is brought to her from remoter areas, almost on a tray. Bulk-delivery trucks daily load the main hopper with any number of feed-formulations, and the cows are fed via mechanized belt lines.

There are increasingly more such slab-like operations around the country, and for many reasons. The intensified land and cow use is financially profitable, since the cow under such restricted physical conditions produces more milk (although for a shorter productive life-span) than she would under more expansive conditions. The dairyman is becoming almost as modified as his cow, since with slab-operations cow and dairyman are equally removed from the land. His drive for intensified immediate production from his mechanized herd intensifies the exploitation of Earth-resources. Since dairymen seldom raise their own feedstuffs, but purchase the products of the soil from distant lands, a constant withdrawal of resources is effected, and an imbalance between land and animal is magnified. Productive land-balance is then attempted through intensified use of all sorts of man-made additives, about which we know very little.

Feed-formulations normally contain fifteen to twenty-five different ingredients that arrive, in bulk, from many parts of the world. Copra, which is dried coconut meat, may come from anywhere in Southeast Asia; linseed meal or soybean meal may come from around New Orleans; fishmeal perhaps from Japan; mineral supplements from almost anywhere in this country or abroad.

In these areas of origin, the cultural practices regarding additive applications to the various crops that are processed into feed ingredients present a multiplicity of inter-relationships about which we know almost nothing. It behooves us to find out.

Nature can put virulence into pathogens much more rapidly than man can put genetic resistance into crop plants. A disease-causing organism can become increasingly potent and widespread faster than man can develop a species of plant capable of resisting the infestation. Meanwhile, the chemical industry is continually called upon to develop additives in man's continuing struggle against nature. Massive doses of additives, about which we know little, are applied to crops and soils with primitive discrimination. Wind-drifts carry some of these massive applications over much of the earth; and we know little of their long-range effects.

The whole point is that we simply do not know. But we can attempt to find out, in a properly planned manner.

This, again, is a deliberate reference to simplicities — without discussing the additive nature of our well-run hospitals fast becoming disease-exchange centers, where virulent strains of staphlococci are evolving by mutation on human targets dosed with additives.

Throughout the world vast research complexes carry on simulated war-games with zealous and self-righteous intensity as each Power prepares itself for what it considers "any eventuality." Vast computer systems, and other tools of the defense-scientific trade, examine permutations and combinations of imagined possibilities and probabilities, terminating hopefully in the theoretical vanquishment of the enemy. And into each calculation enters the Y-factor of the variable constant. Nowhere, it seems, is the Ecology of Man being studied as a science, discipline, art, and hope toward the measure of our days on Earth. Nowhere, it seems, are these research complexes carrying on "peace games" or simulated "peace games" to encourage their Powers to evolve a design– theory for Man on Earth that will obliterate the possibility of total erasure.

It would seem that the cumulative effects of moral fallout throughout science and government have estranged them from mankind, even in terms of simplicities.

If, by permitting the light of knowledge to recede from our simplicities while we seek exotic and narcotic segmenta- tions, we allow the shadow of total erasure to lengthen across us, we will increasingly mistake shadow for substance. Every motion we make will become a caricature in the grotesque foreshortening of our time.

(November 18, 1960)

III

Man the Contaminator

IT IS UNPALATABLE to assume that man, by the fact of his existence, contaminates the resources of his Earth. If this assumption is fact, man is steadily closing in his environment instead of expanding his horizon.

Water is the most prevalent material resource on Earth; yet we probably know less about it than about any of the other physical ingredients necessary for mankind's existence and material progress. The absolute and universal need of water, and its many-faceted applications, hindered the proper study of its availability, its use and abuse. Now that it is becoming an increasingly acute problem over much of the earth, the statistics gather like dust clouds on horizons.

In the inter-relationship of man with his total environment, water — a least common denominator of complexity, sometimes quiet, often turbulent — presents us with an opportunity to evolve a design-theory with broader implications.

Because water is such a personal thing in terms of human need and use, water statistics have little meaning to the individual. To state that, statistically, the average American uses an average of 60 gallons a day for his household needs does not detail the city and rural slum dweller who, despite availability but without indoor plumbing, uses an average of only 10 gallons a day — or the residents of Pasadena, California, an area of water insufficiency, who during a recent 10-day hot spell averaged 450 gallons a day, mainly for their home coolers.

Water is here used as an example of the inter-modification of man and his resources — not necessarily for mutual gain. This inter-modification applies with similar intensity to those who farm thirsty lands through the artificial application of water, and to those in many coastal cities who find discomfort in heavy rainfall. While water, through annual precipitation, is a renewable resource, man is a continuous and intensified contaminator to the point where unadulterated water is rapidly receding from our land.

Those who live in an area of water sufficiency scarcely think about water at all. In an area of water insufficiency, people live with the misplaced faith that the taps will never run dry because science, like the thundering cavalry, will arrive to the rescue.

With the advent of nuclear power many feel that man's historic hope for the conversion of sea-water into fresh water is now close to realization. Actually, it is not. Even assuming no problems in the disposal of radioactive nuclear waste materials from such conversion plants, other waste-disposal problems emerge.

California, for example, uses a little more than 20 million acre-feet of water annually for all its needs. An acre-foot represents the amount of water that will cover one acre to a uniform depth of one foot; this is equivalent to some 325,000 gallons, representing a weight of some 1,360 tons of water.

Let us assume a series of nuclear-powered conversion plants capable of supplying a significant percentage of California's water needs — some 10 percent or two million acre-feet.

The amount of salts that would have to be extracted from sea-water in the conversion of two million acre-feet represent a weight of some 94 million tons or 188 billion pounds. This is a significant waste-disposal problem. Of course, when such conversion plants are close to oceans, the waste-disposal problem is considerably reduced because the salts, with some difficulty and at some cost, can be dumped back into the sea.

What of brackish water reclamation at some distance from the sea? Inland areas certainly hope to reclaim brackish water in at least equivalent quantities. Two million acre-feet of brackish water represent some 8 million tons, or 18 billion pounds, of waste salts. Here the waste-disposal problem is of marked significance. If stockpiled on the ground much of this waste will inevitably find its way into wells, streams, and rivers, to contaminate usable water in much the same manner that industrial wastes dumped upstream contaminate water supplies many miles downstream.

While we know something about bacterial pollution and the decontamination effects of water moving through soils, we know little in this regard about chemical pollutants. For example: when bacteria-infested water is dumped into a well dug in certain types of soils, the bacteria seldom travel more than 100 feet, horizontally, so that a well dug 100 feet away from the dump-well for the purpose of collecting the seepage may actually accumulate bacteria-free water. Vast quantities of sewage water are currently purified and used for domestic purposes quite safely. Despite recent incidences of enteric viral infections resulting from the domestic use of such water, our government maintains that no enteric disease other than infectious hepatitis has been shown to be waterborne, and that aggressive studies are now being maintained to control this disease.

Chemical contaminants are, however, more complex. Knowledge of how long they remain in soils and of their movements through water is rather sketchy. In the Midwest, a manufacturing plant disposes of its calcium chloride wastes into an adjacent stream meandering into the Ohio River — miles away. Communities a hundred miles and more downstream are being adversely affected by this calcium chloride, even when they extract their water supply from gravel deposits alongside the river. The moving waters did not purify themselves. Near Sacramento, California, potassium and ammonium perchlorate waste materials were dumped onto abandoned mine-tailing deposits, from whence they contaminated the ground-water for miles around. These perchlorates were dumped in concentrations of some 3,500 to 5,000 parts-per-million. Perchlorates, however, are toxic to many plants in concentrations of only one to two parts-per-million.

There are hundreds of similar examples from the industrial, agricultural, and domestic uses of various ingredients; and these, in turn, are only a minute portion of the interrelated problems of water.

Industrial expansion inevitably compounds the complexity of chemical contamination. This is so in our country and will, of course, be so in the less-developed areas of the world as these areas approach the whirlpool of technical progress.

Saline water conversion through the uses of nuclear energy is not the Aladdin's Lamp it appears to be, but presents problems in need of solution now, before the advent of such conversion devices.

While many of these problems are of a scientific–technical nature, many of the problems are far beyond the scientific realm. For example: watershed protection is one of the foundations for proper water management, and one of the major forces stemming encroachment on the wildlands. When seawater conversion becomes actuality, what will happen to the watersheds presently protected from man-made contaminations? Or to the balance of nature in the hitherto relatively unprotected wildlands because they are part of the watershed? Or to fish and game? Or to a walk in the woods? If, through conversion techniques, watershed protection is no longer needed, will then the same science that extracts uncontaminated water from the sea encourage the contamination of other natural resources? There is an inter-relationship here between conversion techniques and wildland preservation that needs to be evaluated; it is only one of many inter-relationships. It would seem that at least a proportionate amount of effort should be expended for such evaluations from the total effort devoted to the saline-conversion devices themselves.

Incidentally, saline water, by definition, is water that contains more than 1,000 parts-per-million of dissolved solids, regardless of the composition of the solids. It is not necessarily a salty — a sodium chloride — water. For comparison purposes: fresh water contains from zero to 1,000 ppm of dissolved solids; sewage effluents contain an additional 100 ppm of the solids of fresh water in which they are carried; brackish water contains from 1,000 to 4,000 ppm of dissolved solids; salted water, 4,000 to 18,000 ppm; and sea water contains 18,000 to 35,000 ppm. The Great Salt Lake, for example, contains 200,000-plus ppm of dissolved solids.

The inter-relationship of water with technical progress is so complex that only gradually are we becoming aware of its implications. Emerging from this awareness is the realization that how water is used is everyone's concern since, to a large extent, we use each other's water. Most of the country now consumes water that has previously been used at least once, and often five and six times before it emerges with the twist of the tap. The fact that water is re-used does not necessarily make it unpalatable or of poor quality. It does mean that greater caution and more astute planning must be exercised, beginning with the first use of the water and continuing through its numerous re-uses as it wends its way eventually to the sea.

We leg-band birds in the study of their migrations. Why could we not label water at the source of first use and study its migrations and modifications? We possess techniques that enable us to secure this information as an additional tool in proper planning.

Of course, the gap between knowing what to do and doing it is often too broad for bridging with existing concepts of responsibility.

One example of an insufficient concept of responsibility is the use of synthetic detergents, rapidly accelerated during the past ten years. Most detergents eventually find their way into surface and ground waters where they do not lend themselves to biochemical breakdown. As a result, detergents often cause foaming at the tap, turbidity in the water glass, off-taste in the mouth, and bad odors throughout. Often they cause foaming on lake surfaces and alongside riverbanks similar in appearance to rather large icebergs. The surface-active ingredient of most synthetic detergents is a material known as alkyl-benzene-sulfonate, or ABS. A new type of ABS has been around for several years that does lend itself to a rather substantial biochemical breakdown. Some 70 percent of the old type can be degraded, or broken down, compared with some 95 percent of the new type. Attempts have been made in this country and in England to convince detergent manufacturers to use the new type ABS, with almost no success. It seems that the old type has certain manufacturing advantages. When detergent recycling becomes intensively and extensively unacceptable to water users, some restrictive measures will probably be attempted. But why should industry wait for restrictive measures when proper planning and responsibility could be effective now? Why should responsibility await restriction?

The entire source of fresh water on Earth is from precipitation, from rainfall and from snow-pack. Our country is enormously blessed with a renewable supply of fresh water. We receive, year after year, enough fresh water through precipitation, on an average, to cover the entire country to a depth of around 30 inches. Of course, we seldom get it where or when we want it. Of the 30 inches, some 21 inches return to the atmosphere as evapo-transpiration; the remaining nine inches is our manageable annual water supply, of which we use approximately three inches, while the remainder meanders to the sea.

Actually, the measurement of rainfall and snowpack as an indication of water availability is somewhat primitive. Water availability must be related to need; and need increases as population increases and industry expands. Demand for water from a so-called normal rainfall and snowpack has increased dramatically in the past several years. Industry and housing seeking climatic ease in semi-arid areas multiply this need enormously. Timber depletion, stream pollution, deep-well pumping for irrigation, accelerated water demands to fight forest fires caused by increasing numbers of vacationers using campsites — the list and inter-relationship goes on and on with increasing complexity.

A new term, perhaps water-use or water-ply, could define the supply of water available for use. This term would take into account population increases, industry expansion, water pollution, agricultural needs, runoff acceleration, as well as rainfall and snowpack availabilities and ground-water quan-

tities. An equation can be written to take all these factors
into account, and to permit variations of these factors as they
occur, as withdrawals and additions are made. A water-ply
of 100, for example, would mean a sufficiency of water from
all sources for all the year's needs; 110 would indicate a 10
percent surplus; 90, a 10 percent deficiency. We would then
have current knowledge regarding our water resources, on a
regional, national, and international basis.

We have tremendous water resources — and tremendous
losses. In the 17 Western States, for example, water losses
from evapo-transpiration could irrigate at least 13 million
acres of farmland, which is equivalent to the total area cultivated annually in Japan. Some slight measures are being
taken to reduce this loss in our water-short West. One of
the confounding aspects is that precisely those areas that
are good for farming are the ones that are short of water to
begin with.

Of our total irrigated farmland in the United States, more
than 40 percent is located in the West. The fecund valleys
and dry climate of our Western States permit year-'round
farming and continued harvest if the land is properly irrigated. New techniques are spreading the use of farm irrigation to the Eastern half of our country at a rate that is
actually alarming. The development of sprinkler irrigation
systems so that corn can be planted on hillsides that previously were left in natural cover can be harmful rather than
beneficial. Corn, native to this hemisphere, now rings our
planet; and hillside corn is now one of the heaviest contribu-
tors to man-made soil erosion, depletion, and actual hunger.

With proper advanced planning we could achieve proper
utilization of our spent water. In England, where there is
a somewhat symbiotic relationship between industrial and
agricultural land-use, and where irrigation is not a great
need, sludge sewage is used quite extensively, to the point
where some 350,000 tons are annually applied to farmland,

essentially for its fertilizer effects. This represents some 10,000 tons of nitrogen; 5,000 tons of phosphorus; and 1,200 tons of potassium. Israel's planning calls for the transport of sewage-effluent from Tel Aviv to the Negev, 60 miles away, in sufficient quantities to irrigate 50,000 acres. Israel is as much concerned with the soil nutrients in the effluent as it is with the water. In Australia, wastes are transported forty or so miles from Melbourne to irrigate some 14,000 acres. We in this country are using sewage-effluent for crop irrigation, but in an extremely limited manner. In the United States, it should be noted, sanitation standards do not permit the use of raw sewage in truck farming; and even where treated effluent is used on crops that are cooked by the processor, such water is withheld from these crops for 20 to 45 days prior to harvest.

Examination of past data reveals that water demand increases approximately twice as rapidly as does population. If the population of the United States doubles within the next fifty years, as many forecast, water demand will increase by four times to some 800 billion gallons a day. This will mean that nearly 75 percent of our daily water runoff will have to be used. This is a fantastically costly contemplation, especially when it has to be accomplished within a brief period of some fifty years. In addition, overall water contamination increases, perhaps even geometrically, with population increases.

Water is the most widely used resource in the world. Its withdrawal-for-use in our country outweighs all other materials by more than a hundredfold. From our daily water use of some 200 billion gallons, almost 10 percent is used by industry, households, and professional services directly through municipal or rural water systems; the remaining 90 percent is used fairly equally between industry and farmland irrigation. These estimates are on a gross basis and include a large re-use. More than 60 percent of all water withdrawn is returned to the ground or streams and can be used again. The remainder is evaporated or consumed. More than 75 percent of this disappearance occurs in the irrigation of land in the Western United States.

Irrigation, basically, is the application of water to land, through man's efforts, for agricultural purposes. While irrigation had its greatest impetus during the past sixty years or so, its history goes deep into antiquity.

In Egypt, where all the cultivated land is irrigated, the first Pharaoh of the First Dynasty introduced it there some 5,000 years ago. In China the unbelievable Imperial Canal, 700 miles long, built 1,200 years ago, was used for navigation as well as for irrigation. In India, considered by many to be the cradle of irrigation practices, the earliest sacred writings in the Vedas referred to various canals, dams, and holding tanks. Rivers used in irrigation procedures were symbolized as sacred cows, and canals taken from them as sacred calves. As early as 300 B.C. the Vishnugupta Kautilaya mentioned that if private dams were neglected for five years their charge was taken over by the State. A rather legitimate alternative, one would say, in an area where people's lives depended upon proper water management. Both the Old and the New Testament refer frequently to irrigation practices. The Justinian Code of Ancient Rome placed strong emphasis on proper irrigation. The tunnel system originated in Iran during the reign of Darius, 2,500 years ago, is still being used today in that country.

Throughout history the artificial watering of crop land occupied much of man's thinking, and new techniques evolved slowly.

The country with the largest area irrigated is China, where some 80 million acres are artificially watered. The second largest is India with some 60 million acres irrigated.

The United States is the third, with some 38 million acres irrigated.

We are a highly industrialized country, with power coursing through national and regional grids over most of our land to supply energy for pumping. China and India are relatively primitive in this regard. It is precisely this pumping power we possess that permits the withdrawal of huge quantities of underground water from hundreds of feet down. However, this power is not necessarily beneficial; it can be quite harmful because of the perverse inevitability related to water and its utilization. For example: underground water reservoirs have accumulated over the centuries; constant seepage and underground percolation add to these highly-efficient natural reservoirs. However, the current rate of withdrawal of this ground water is many times the rate of its replenishment. Cleverly designed pumps and power availability simplify and accelerate this withdrawal. California, for example, has an annual overdraft of ground water of some 2 million acre-feet, which represent the quantity of water withdrawn in excess of its natural or man-induced replacement from these underground reservoirs. This excess withdrawal is reflected in the Santa Clara area below San Francisco where at one time ample groundwater supplies were available at depths of eight feet. Today, people have to drill down more than 200 feet before they reach ground water. In the area west of Fresno, California, the annual decline is anywhere from four feet to 30 feet. Similar declines are occurring in Texas, Arizona, and throughout the country where water extractions exceed water replenishment. Ground water reservoirs are difficult to recharge, and excess withdrawal from them often means a relatively permanent loss. As water tables drop, saline water creeps in from the sea even from many miles away and from nearer salt deposits, until the point is reached where even the best-designed pumps will bring forth only a flow of unusable water. The land gradu-

ally withdraws from the abuse it has received at the hand of
man, who does not plan or accept responsibility for his own
future.

Another aspect of this perverse inevitability is the fact
that when arid lands are reclaimed and deserts are made
fecund, yields often stagger imagination. In order to maintain
high yields there is an increasing dependence upon chemical
fertilizers. Since these chemicals are not totally absorbed by
plants, significant portions, leached out of the soil by irrigation waters, find their way into underground reservoirs where
many of them add to the salinity of the waters. For example:
the average burden of chlorides caried by the Rio Grande
River above El Paso, Texas, is some 50,000 tons a year.
Between El Paso and Fort Quitman approximately 100 miles
downstream, the river waters are used extensively for irrigation, and the chloride load at Fort Quitman is more than three
times as great as the chloride load at El Paso. Furthermore,
spent irrigation waters carry heavy loads of residual insecticides and other chemical additives which, as they drift into
usable water, become pollutants. A point can be reached, and
we are approaching it quite rapidly, where uncontaminated
natural water will become a rarity.

This descending spiral of contaminant-concentration in
ever-falling water tables is the inevitable result of man's
avariciousness. Our concern and demonstrated success with
immediate yield-per-acre increases is not an indication of our
technical abilities nearly so much as it is a manifestation of
our planning weaknesses.

If a symbiotic relationship were encouraged among our
residential, agricultural, and industrial areas, our water availability would become more stabilized. Of course, such a relationship would bring about deep changes, the greatest of
which would be the recognition that man's resources are to
be used wisely and well, for the prolongation of their availability.

If a balance were attempted between residential and farming communities, a sort of cycle would be established where the residue of the cities would become the prime usable resources for the farmlands. With proper planning a community of 50,000, for example, would be able, through its spent waters, to irrigate several thousand acres of farmland and supply it with fertilizers and other soil nutrients. Such an arrangement would generate major economic savings both to the city dweller and to the farmer. In a sense, the city community here becomes a converter for the farm community, as each supplies the other with basic ingredients necessary for life.

Perhaps existing patterns are too deeply entrenched for major change in this regard to be realized. However, communities should be encouraged to plan in this direction for the future.

A major vegetable-growing-and-processing complex in the rich New Jersey farmlands has been utilizing a closed, or recycling, system for several years with excellent results. In this system the wastes resulting from the processing plants, and from the residential communities related to these plants, are returned to the growing lands as renewable water and excellent fertilizers. Special irrigation patterns and pumps were designed to achieve this purpose. The entire operation is highly profitable and the land remains in excellent production; resources and money are saved.

In the West, which is really a world test-laboratory, because of the conditions of weather, water, crops, and population movements, cannery wastes are mainly unused and present an ever-mounting disposal problem. Closed, or recycled, systems are a major necessity in the West. It is to be hoped that eventual restrictive measures may force them upon industry, which thus far functions with grave irresponsibility

in this direction. But must industry await restrictive measures before accepting responsibility?

We like to think of ourselves as a nation of planners. Our
increasingly turbulent water problems offer excellent opportunities to demonstrate whatever planning skills we do
possess.

Of course, if our base line of reference toward our resources
were recognized, we could plan for their proper utilization.
But this requires an awareness we do not seem to possess at
this time.

People have always migrated, often in vast numbers, from
areas of scarcity to areas of adequacy or hoped-for adequacy.
It is likely that similar migrations may wander for years in
search of water abundance, and find only adequacy and
inevitable scarcity, unless we learn how to use our possessions
properly.

It would seem that unplanned acceleration of technical
progress always accelerates contamination. When the con-
taminators do not recognize themselves as such, can they be
charged with the responsibility of cleansing themselves?

And who will charge them with such responsibility if they
do not recognize their own roles?

Must we, regardless of unpalatability, assume that man
is essentially a contaminator of everything he touches?

It would seem that this is one of the basic questions for
man's continued existence on Earth.

(January 27, 1961)

VI

IV

The Atomic Philanderers

THE GAP BETWEEN knowledge and wisdom is often widened rather than bridged by experts and specialists; this is nowhere more manifest than in the darkening confusion generated and encouraged by our atomic philanderers throughout the world.

The brilliance of the nuclear flash has brought a new age of ignorance into being; and the dark glasses worn by observers placed at safe distance from Point Zero, to protect their vision from blindness, seem to have become a permanent part of the structure of the leaders of man's hope and destiny. In the semi-haze which these leaders have made, sharpness of thought and purpose is frayed and unravelled.

The light that exposed vast new areas to knowledge also exposed vast new dangers; and in one flash we took a fear-

some backward leap in man's eternal struggle for survival —
as though from a suddenly opened and endless pit. The self-
defeating law of destructive might has never been more in
force than today, and its contradiction generates such confusion — even among many of those who desire to dispel the
descending darkness — that they rush into their own caves
of specialization from whence they flash pencil-thin lights
in intermittent and haphazard fashion, perhaps hoping that
thereby salvation will be guided to them.

The evaluation of the beneficial and harmful aspects of
nuclear devices — a tool that cannot be erased from man's
arsenal of abilities — continues in a segmented manner only.
It is neither fortunate nor unfortunate but fact that any consideration of Man on Earth today obviously has, as its foundation, man's relationship to the nuclear energy he has
exposed and with which he has not yet learned to live. The
least common denominator for human survival is not in the
specific ingredients of man's environment — water, land, air,
food, and his continuing translation of Earth's resources into
human use — but exists within his arsenal of abilities.

It is the contention here that our most urgent need, from
scientists, leaders, and ourselves, is a total evaluation of the
Ecology of Man; that, in order to evolve a design-theory for
Man on Earth, we must use to the full the abilities and
resources we now possess; that we begin to do so without
delay, in the name of sanity, and for the continuation of the
species.

This is not a jeremiad. It is an attempt to extract meaning
and purpose in this deeply personal search for the dignity of
life. If the god, Science, parades nakedly across the face of
the earth, let it be said he is unfrocked. If the god, Politicus,
wants to make a personal plaything of man's fate and hope
in order that he and his brother-gods can heap waste upon
each other, let them be identified by their stench.

To be alive with dignity is a good thing; to live with fear is not.

For more than fifteen years we have had a genetic inbreeding of the gods Science and Politicus, and their matings have resulted in so many idiocies that we are almost accepting chaos as a way of life.

Does this truly make sense to a species that birthed Beethoven, Leonardo, Shakespeare — and you?

It is possible for the world's scientific community to take upon itself responsibility for its actions; and it is possible for scientists to think of man as a total human being, living with full capacity — so to be honored, cherished, and respected. A few attempt to do so, but the many do not because of cynicism, arrogance, stupidity, fear, or corruption. Many hunt headlines rather than knowledge; many stalk fund allocations for pet projects rather than ideas; many seek refuge in the remote areas of their minds and consciences, hoping there to remain undisturbed and unresponsible for their deeds. Such unresponsibility is probably a major factor in the generation and spread of scientific irresponsibility.

The genteel savagery of the scientific cynic — hiding behind the barbed-wire curtained weaponry compounds throughout the world — is the curse of this age.

At one time the minds of many men were concerned with the number of angels that could dance on the head of a pin, and they cited chapter and verse from whatever reference materials they had available. Today, from our vantage point we can look down history upon such minds with amusement at their beguiling primitiveness. Today, the minds of many men are concerned with the numbers of people that may, or can, be annihilated through a given intensity of a nuclear barrage; and they, too, cite computer chapter-and-verse from whatever reference data they have available. Will history ever be able to look down upon such minds with any feeling but contempt and abomination?

Yet this need not be so.

If the scientific community were to deny its favors to its queer bedfellow, the god of Politics, in much the same manner and for the same purpose that Aristophanes' heroine Lysistrata and her colleagues 2,500 years ago denied their favors to their warring child-men so long as they sought war, science could regain its dignity and freedom to serve all mankind.

Why is there so much concern with nuclear devices over and above other clever devices calculated to exterminate mankind? Actually, the biochemical warfare complexes throughout the world are equally, and perhaps even more diabolically, prepared to deliver massive and indiscriminate annihilation. Clouds of poison — invisible, odorless, tasteless, and deadly — can descend undetected, without that fearsome flash, and silently kill every living being within the wind-drifting target area. Scientists and technicians responsible for and involved in this savagery apparently feel little more concern with the way they earn their living than if they were baking bread.

Does the concern with nuclear devices stem mainly from the vast and indiscriminate numbers of people that can be killed, and from the valid thread of total erasure?

Perhaps.

However, of at least equal significance is the dilemma presented by nuclear energy — a dilemma compounded by scientists; and now — since science has become a worldwide cult — a dilemma permeating the world. Perhaps, if the nature of nuclear energy were solely destructive, we could, through human awareness and conscience, isolate this weapon and identify those who seek to fatten themselves through the destructive consumption of their fellow man.

But nuclear energy, as well as being destructive, has magnificent constructive uses for mankind. It can supply power to areas of need throughout the world. It can, at some point, extract usable waters from the seas. It can release man from animal-toil. Radioactive isotopes are now broadly used in medicine as an aid in the diagnosis of certain ailments and as a measurement of the effectiveness of certain treatments.

It could be used constructively in the study of water. The available supply of usable water is of increasing concern throughout much of the world and most of the United States. Statistics have indicated that unless new sources become available in rather large quantities, water will be in short supply throughout most of the country by 1975. The greatest natural wastage of water is by plants known as phreatophytes. Phreatophytes are water-loving plants whose roots tap the water table and the soil directly above it. In the Western United States, where water supply is already a grave problem, it is estimated that phreatophytes grow on some 16 million acres and discharge, through transpiration, some 20 million to 25 million acre-feet of water annually. By comparison, the current total water requirements for all of California — for its agricultural, industrial and domestic needs — are somewhat around 22 million acre-feet annually. At this stage of knowledge, water and soil scientists do not yet know how ground-water is actually absorbed by root systems, or the rates of uptake of water by the different phreatophytes, or the consumptive use of water by different plants in various hydrologic environments. Suitable radioactive tracers, with very short half-lives, could quite likely help secure the knowledge necessary to retain for use much of this generally wasted 20 million to 25 million acre-feet of water annually. Unfortunately, very little is currently being done about this particular problem.

Our life-supporting topsoil is being drained off at an accelerated rate; it flows as silt and sediment through tidal
estuaries and into the sea. We know little of the mechanics
of sediment-transport. Even the generally accepted idea that
sediment moves at precisely the flow-rate of the water in
which it is suspended remains unproven. Radioactive isotopes can be used to trace sediment movement and sediment
mechanics, especially in alluvial streams in our needed search
to retain the wealth of the land.

When this country was young it contained a land mass of
1,900 million acres. In the short life of the United States
more than 280 million acres of land have been destroyed to
productivity, and erosion is actively destructive on another
775 million acres. For comparison purposes, California has a
total area of 100 million acres. Altogether it is estimated that
of the original nine inches of topsoil with which our country
was blessed when the nation was founded, one-third has been
washed away. It takes nature from 300 to 1,000 years and
more to bring back a single inch of topsoil. We sometimes lose
more than that over a given area in a single heavy rainstorm
when our streams and rivers run murky with the run-off
wealth of the land. The knowledge that can be acquired
through radioactive sediment studies can be used as a tool to
help us devise plans for the most efficient use of our close-in
lands, so rapidly becoming entombed in concrete. Almost
nothing is being done about such studies at this time. Our
scientists are occupied with other, considerably less useful
matters.

There are many areas in the field of natural resources —
and of course in many other fields — where nuclear energy
could have vital uses for mankind.

Yet the scientists who helped release this primordial energy
labored, literally, for destruction. Even those who were aware
of the beneficial aspects of nuclear energy accepted, perhaps
with sadness, that these beneficial aspects would be only the

residue, the remainder, left over from their achievements. They accepted as a way of life the concept that their prime activity was for destruction, and that only their waste product, as it were, might contain a potentiality for human enrichment. This dilemma, resulting from scientific expediency and the submergence of scientific objectivity, was inevitable once science became wedded to a policy of, and to a search for, destruction. The cynical ceremony has, of itself, birthed a generation of scientific irresponsibles. This dilemma was compounded when the bomb exploded and scientists labelled their project "completed and ready for Phase II" even while they knew that their knowledge was incomplete and their reports unfinished.

Year after year scientific objectivity has been drained into the coffers of industry and government; and scientists themselves have begun to believe that an unlimited supply of money buys an unlimited amount of brains. Many hie themselves to the source of this unlimited money supply, where their recently achieved godhood permits them to elbow their way to the head of the trough. Once there, they bow their heads drink their fill.

It should not be that way.

Science is supposed to clarify, not to compound confusion. Those who accepted science as their guide toward a better and a richer life fear their guide is blinded by his own brilliance and is leading them in darkness into strange and fearsome areas, with no assurance of, and little hope for, a safe emergence.

The atomic philanderers have given to the world a gift of fear, not of clarity. The same science that proudly searches the heavens for knowledge and a measure of its own eternity shamefully recommends that man dig for himself caves in the earth as a measure for his own survival. This, too, is a compounding of the nuclear dilemma.

The hideous blending of science and fear generated the moral fallout referred to earlier. While scientists, as a caste, are probably more altered by moral fallout than the remainder of the social body, since devastation, especially to warfare scientists, is a principle and a creed, the cumulative effects of moral fallout have spread insidiously throughout the entire body of mankind, even to the very young.

Scientists should be able to pursue projects emerging from themselves, from their own sensitivity and their historic objectivity, not projects foisted upon them by others for personal gain.

Objectivity does not mean irresponsibility; quite the contrary. It is expediency which permits scientists to shirk their responsibilities and enables them to claim that their actions are dictated to them by others as a matter of public need — which is now so often unrelated to human need. Expediency, by its nature, forces a synthetic isolation upon the scientist. Objectivity, however, demands the total evaluation of thought and action. Objectivity is a principled pursuit. Expediency is an emotional search unguided by principle.

By enslaving man to a continued environment of fear, scientists have chained themselves. Their brittle and piercing disharmonies, almost above the scale for human tolerance, confront us with new measurements — as though the foot were now 13 inches and the minute 55 seconds, retroactive to the beginnings of time — and with new dimensions of value within which increased knowledge brings increased fear; and with new technical brilliance which brings a darkening of wisdom.

This, too, is a compounding of the nuclear dilemma confronting us all.

Scientific responsibility toward man should be the most essential ingredient in the search for knowledge; and the physicist who seeks to wage nuclear war should become suspect, even as a physicist, since his credo is expediency and his scientific objectivity suspect. The entire spectrum of science presents similar examples.

We recognize that medical researchers who alter a drug just enough to enable pharmaceutical companies to re-label, re-price, and secure stronger patent-protection are obviously suspect in terms of their scientific objectivity. We recognize the same suspicion toward physicians who then, out of scientific laziness or ignorance, prescribe these drugs as new.

When the scientist speaks of matters beyond his specialty he is justly expected to utilize, as a method of approach, his scientific training toward objectivity, toward a responsible search for knowledge. If he does not do so, he has revealed himself as being so compartmentalized and segmented that he has no frame of reference to reality or knowledge or responsibility — even regarding his specialty — and he should be suspect.

Why can we not attempt to achieve some simplicities toward this nuclear dilemma, so that fear could be banished and we could then live our lives with a measure of dignity?

Why cannot the scientific community present to the world, in language not jargon, the total spectrum of its present knowledge regarding the dangers and benefits of nuclear energy?

Why can we not attempt to weigh benefit against danger in an attempt to determine just how much out of balance they are and whether or not, at our present state of knowledge, balance could be achieved?

The United Nations, without piercing or threatening the sovereignty of its member and non-member nations, could certainly sponsor an International Commission on Nuclear Evaluation.

Throughout his history man risked danger in an attempt to achieve purpose. Perhaps, if the facts concerning nuclear energy were exposed to world-knowledge the dangers might be considered worth the risks in light of the benefits that might be achieved. And perhaps not. At least some sort of balance sheet would be drawn against which we could measure our nuclear dilemma.

An International Commission on Nuclear Evaluation would have no need and no reason to pry into the military secrets of nations. It would not sit in judgment on one nation or another. It would be a Commission of scientific objectivity and responsibility that would publicly detail the beneficial and harmful aspects of nuclear energy — this tool that cannot be erased from man's arsenal of abilities.

Nobel Laureates come from many countries and represent many skills. Perhaps these men can form, under the auspices of the United Nations or even the Nobel Committee, the basic Commission on Nuclear Evaluation. Unanimous, majority, and dissenting findings would be made public by this Commission at yearly intervals. Discussions by scientists and non-scientists could be generated throughout the world by such Commission findings, and a revitalized scientific objectivity and responsibility would emerge.

There is no jeopardy for any nation's sovereignty, plans, or goals in such an International Commission on Nuclear Evaluation. Perhaps, if this first step were taken, other logical measures would follow. We risk no danger here, and we can achieve great purpose.

In the full span of human vision man can detect some 20,000 variations of color, ranging in gradations from red, orange, yellow, green, blue, indigo, and violet. This is the visible spectrum. Some researchers now believe that the human eye can detect some 40,000 variations within this visible spectrum.

All light is measured in wavelengths, either in millimicrons or in Angstrom Units. Violet, at the lower end of the visible spectrum, has a wavelength of approximately 400 millimicrons, or 4,000 Angstrom Units. Red, at the upper end of the visible spectrum, has a wavelength of approximately 700 millimicrons, or 7,000 Angstrom Units.

Everything visible to the human eye, whether on Earth or in the heavens, whether to a great artist or to a finger-painting child, is visible only within the 400 to 700 millimicron range. Within these 300 millimicrons, or 3,000 Angstrom Units, the 20,000 to 40,000 variations can be detected by man.

Yet man actually uses a wavelength range many times broader than the narrow band available for his physical vision. He cannot see these other wavelengths except through instrumentation and devices. They are present in his physical universe; he is aware of their existence even though he realizes the incompleteness of his knowledge of them; and he has learned some of their uses and some of their dangers.

The ultraviolet range alone reaches downward from some 4,000 Angstrom Units to around 10, a range much broader than our visible spectrum. And below ultraviolet is the X-ray range, then the gamma-ray, and finally the secondary cosmic-ray ranges.

Between violet, at the lowest range of the visible spectrum, and the far depths of the secondary cosmic rays, lies a wavelength span of more than a million Angstrom Units. A similar span exists from the red of the upper band of the visible spectrum through the invisible far infrared ranges.

In the broad expanse from the lowest to the farthest ranges of the spectrum, man's physical vision functions only in the minute segment of around 3,000 Angstrom Units. Yet he can utilize for his betterment, although often at measurable risk, vastly greater segments from either end of his visible spectrum.

This is perhaps an object lesson.

In the lower ranges of the invisible spectrum, X-rays are useful, yet they can be harmful if they are not used with skill. X-rays can be diagnostic and therapeutic; but when used indiscriminately and to excess they can be deadly.

In the upper ranges of the invisible spectrum, infrared can be equally diagnostic, therapeutic, and deadly. The near-infrared ranges are being used diagnostically for many purposes in the field of natural resources, particularly in agriculture, to determine areas of plant diseases and crop deficiencies, yield-forecasting and water-studies, fertilizer-response and soil-capacities. The middle and far infrared ranges may be used hopefully in medical diagnosis at some point, if certain theories recently formulated are borne out by further research. In that event, risks from the X-rays of the lower invisible spectrum may be eliminated by the proper utilization of the upper invisible spectrum.

Man frequently demonstrates that he can bridge vast unseen ranges; that his scope is beyond immediacy; that his vision is far beyond that which is presented only to his physical eye.

What of the total spectrum of nuclear energy — the least common denominator for man's survival and for the evaluation of himself and his total environment in this age? We know something of its visible implications, of its obvious dangers and its obvious values. What of the lower and upper ranges of the invisible spectrum of nuclear energy? Are they equally as vast, by comparison, as the invisible wavelengths? And do they have similar implications? What of the infra-manifestations and the ultra-manifestations of this primordial energy so recently harnessed and so rapidly grown almost beyond our control?

Man presented this energy to his world in a single brilliant flame. Will it be memorialized as the Flash of Recognition, a monument to progress and man's upward climb? Or must we accept it as a flame searing our vision, dimming our visible spectrum, and condemning us to live in semi-haze?

There yet remains a great measure of free choice.

(January 13, 1961)

V

Man the Modifier

MAN IS A constant modifier of himself, and his environment, continually risking, through ignorance or avarice, his ability to survive.

One of the three basic requirements for the continued survival of any organism is its ability to recuperate from whatever exertions it expends. If it cannot recuperate, its extinction is inevitable. This is as true of the city human organism as of the rain forest vegetative organism. The other two basic requirements are nourishment and reproduction.

Man, the constant modifier of natural processes, affects his own recuperative capabilities and those of his environment. For man, recuperation is considerably more than a physical process. We may more readily solve the problems of population-pressure and food-supply than those of our increasingly complex physical and nonphysical recuperative environment and capacity.

Each descending step man takes into the maze of dependence upon technical involvements hinders the simplicity of his recuperation; and the more materially complex a society becomes, the more complex are the recuperative processes, to the point where survival itself may become increasingly doubtful. It is quite possible for the daily complexity of living to demand exertions from which the human organism cannot recuperate soon enough before further exertions for survival are demanded of it. When this happens without relief, death is accelerated. When a society suffers attrition of its recuperative needs, the probability of extinction is accelerated.

We have numerous examples of this in bio-ecology, Earth-resource exploitation, animal experimentation, and in the daily processes of living.

There are many varieties of hummingbirds that must go into deep hibernation at night in order to survive. They are equipped to feed only during the day, and not during the night. Their exertions for food-accumulation are so great that during the time they cannot feed themselves they can only recuperate and survive by going into a comatose condition. When, in the properly equipped laboratory, daylight conditions are simulated and the proper plants are made available, the hummingbird will attempt to feed itself until it is overcome by exhaustion.

In nutritional experimentation it is possible to prepare an animal feed-ration high enough in nutritional value — but so immensely imbalanced in terms of mass — that the animal will expend all its energies in feed-ingestion, leaving little reserve for other body functions. When it attempts to recuperate, it becomes increasingly weak until it lacks sufficient energy even to rise from its resting position.

Where dairy cows are kept penned and are properly fed and exercised rather than permitted to roam, even for good forage, milk-production from the animal will increase in some cases by more than 10 percent. This has been proven numerous times in this country, and in Britain, Holland, Germany, Scandinavia, and Peru. Always, when exertion and recuperation are kept in some sort of balance, maximum animal-yield can be expected. Increased exertions reduce yield as do extended periods of enforced rest. The fatigue factor involved in the enforced rest of the individual is gradually being recognized as a hindrance to normal recuperative processes.

In the rain forest, the lush green treetop-cover usually canopies soil that is extremely impoverished and suitable only for the types of vegetation it supports. When cattle owners or farmers cut down and burn the trees to wrest clearings for pasture or crops the land becomes sterile — usually within two or three years. Removal of the trees permits the tropical rains to pelt the unprotected soil with full fury, and the resultant gully and sheet-erosion wreak havoc. Families then remove themselves and their livestock to other areas, where the process is repeated. If left to itself, the rain forest may recuperate from its man-enforced exertions in from 100 to 200 years. If not left to itself, if clearings are extended deeper into the forest adjacent to the exploited land, sterility spreads; and since the recuperative base is weakened, recuperation itself may become impossible. The fecundity of tropical rain forest soils has always been more story than fact. Madagascar, now the Malagásy Republic, once forest-covered, is now more than 75 percent denuded; and tropical areas in both hemispheres show similar depredations. On the continent of Africa the forest is everywhere in retreat because of population pressures, accelerated commercial exploitation, and destructive agricultural practices. Africa is becoming known as the Dying Land. It is a bitter dilemma that the people of Africa, after centuries, are emerging from human exploitation only to face past and present exploitation of their Earth-resources which have been depleted to the point where the continent may not be able to sustain its inhabitants.

Primitive exertions permit primitive recuperative processes which are effective. However, the complexity of contemporary man's exertion demands increasingly complex recuperative processes which become decreasingly effective. Recuperation for man now demands constant considerations of ethical and moral concepts in addition to the biologic needs of his organism; this is so precisely because man, for the first time in his history, faces the constant threat of total erasure. The morality of our time has not kept pace with the techniques of our time. The controllers of man's fate are the spokesmen of technique, not of the morality and dignity of the individual.

This age of anxiety is consuming itself mainly because of the decreasing ability of man to recuperate, as an individual, from his physical, emotional, and spiritual expenditures. The various medical and nonmedical involvements in the problems of anxiety cannot eliminate man's decreasing recuperative capabilities as the basic cause of individual torsion — of personal stress and strain toward himself and his environment. The human ecologic factors, the inter-relationship of man as a total human being with his total environment, must be understood before any measures can even hope to be corrective.

Man's involvement is increasingly with groups of people, goods, and services, and with group-concepts that attempt to cater to his physical and nonphysical needs. Recuperation, however, is a purely individual function for which there is no substitute and no transference.

The reference here is not primarily to the mechanical involvements with all sorts of gadgetry, which is inescapable.

There is probably a growing awareness that devices do not simplify life but create a dependence upon forces about which we know little, and upon people about whom we know even less. The modern electrified house is a gadget-ridden complex whose actual function as a home depends upon strangers and impersonal services rather than upon the family unit for which, theoretically, it was built, or which presently occupies it.

Most forms of entertainment are designed for group-enticement rather than for individual stimulation. Our educational systems, and local, state, and federal governments are, at their best, involved with group-concepts and not at all with individual need. Even prepaid health plans are designed for groups and not individuals. Actually, many physician-administrators in prepaid medicine express the belief that for the proper function of their plans the well members who require no attention and services are assets to the medical group, while those in need of attention are a liability. While this is a meretricious concept, most such groups continue to function with assembly-line time-and-motion efficiency. Prepaid group medicine, initiated with high purpose to meet a growing individual need, struggled courageously against organized medical opposition until it, too, became a highly-organized medical and business complex.

The point here is that our society is becoming increasingly incapable of concerning itself with individuals. We are, certainly, a society of increasing mechanical ease, mechanical simplicity, and mechanical acquisition. We are also a society of increasing anxiety and individual torsion.

The direct relationship between these two factors is essentially the nature of our recuperative processes. Gadgetry does not simplify life because it does not simplify comprehension; on the contrary, it compounds dependence and dilutes the individual's internal resources. We accept mechanical complexity as a way of life, and are willing and often anxious to embrace this complexity in the tortured hope that it will simplify life. We know less and less about the things we depend upon for our ease. As a result, we increase our dependence upon others to build and maintain these devices, payment for which requires our exertion; and we depend less and less upon our own resources for our individual ease and recuperation. Yet mass-recuperation is as impossible as mass-nourishment or mass-reproduction; these are purely personal functions, individual to each of us. In this technical age man recedes even from the comprehension of his basic needs — a recession which results in his not understanding himself and his environment, and in a feeling of separation from his environment.

We are in an age of seeming plenty, yet, swamped by uncertainty, we look back nostalgically at the seemingly simpler and richer life of our forebears. Despite mechanized ease few of us do what we want to do, or even know what it is that we want to do. We constantly face so many things that simply have to be done before we can go on to the next item on our personal agendas that we drift from one thing to the next, with little direction and less free time to ourselves to verify our bearings.

Our recuperative capacities seem insignificant when measured against our physical and nonphysical exertion-expenditures. We are constantly paying out, from the reservoir of our strength, for so many things we later find we do not really need, that were not worth the exertions we expended for them. When we finally do achieve some sort of wisdom toward ourselves and the needs of our lives for personal enrichment, we find our reservoir nearly empty, or else silted with a glutinous mass from which we cannot extricate ourselves because our strength has become dissipated.

In the jungled maze of mechanized living we cut down and burn our canopies to wrest clearings for ourselves and our hopes; and then, when life's fury erodes the soil from which we seek nourishment, we cut down and burn the adjacent canopy until we have cut a swath of sterility through our lives that horrifies us when we later take a backward glance.

Why do we continually exert ourselves to decide between choices that are so often undifferentiated? There's little difference between one brand of low-priced automobile and another, and even less between one gasoline and another. There often is no difference at all between one brand of canned fruit and another, except for the label, where both have been identically processed in the same cannery, as so often happens. Most of our material and nonmaterial choices are between one and another sort of undifferentiation.

Since we exert effort, we should certainly strive to make intelligent differentiations and choices that have some meaning for us.

We exert ourselves toward the acquisition of leisure, which we are securing in increasing quantity. But leisure is not at all recuperation. Leisure is freedom from gainful employment and has little to do with recuperative processes. The exertion expended in leisure is fabulous. We are consumers of a leisure as prepackaged and marketed as any other mass-produced item. In a society that produces material goods to excess, leisure becomes an economic force demanding a vast and costly movement of people and goods. Despite mechanical ease and increased leisure, we are more restricted and more compartmentalized in terms of personal growth than most of us care to admit.

Of course, we are in an age of push-button material plenty; of prepackaged ideas; of the 17-day-17-city packaged foreign tour; of constant motion — as though we fear to be quiet. The people of the United States now travel, within our continental boundaries alone, some three trillion miles a year: a haze of constant motion, with people simulating ball bearings in a raceway. We have become similar to the man who

paces up and down a corridor all day, checks his pedometer
and says: Look how far I have traveled today.

Of course, too, each increase in motion brings a decrease
in angle of vision, and an increase in tunnel vision. Today,
on our raceway, each man is his own enemy if he takes his
eyes off the road to scan the passing scene; each man's neighbor is his enemy if one of them drives over the dividing line.

It seems that governments and people all over the world,
East and West, wish to emulate the United States in terms
of material success. This seems to be the goal, as well as the
definition, of progress: more things for more people. However, such progress carries with it the virulent germs of
infectious anxiety precisely because such progress, by extend-
ign the twisting maze of daily living, inevitably dilutes man's
recuperative capabilities.

An age of material surplus is inevitably an age of material
and nonmaterial undifferentiation. It is as though mass-man
must be smoothed to eliminate any resistance that might
interfere with the flow of progress. The rough protuberances
of individualism cannot be tolerated if the mass is to move
along its greased path.

It is not only that such a society, as a group, becomes
increasingly incapable of concerning itself with the individual, but that it soon reaches a point where it must consider
the individual as its primary enemy. Even those individuals
aware of an attack by society cannot realistically simplify
their lives by separating themselves from this society. This
is a bitter dilemma. However, the search for individual sim-
plification must be constant and vigorous, otherwise one
faces personal chaos.

Another and equally bitter dilemma is that the individual
who strives to retain his individuality must exert himself considerably more than his mass-contemporaries, who seem to

acquire what they want without too much complexity or difficulty. Since his exertion is greater, he needs greater recuperative capabilities and opportunities if he is to continue as an individual. If not, he will succumb, despite struggle, into the mass. But how often does the individual, who is actually the major hope for the survival of man, have such capacities and opportunities? Much too seldom, one would say.

Difference for the mere sake of difference is spurious. The reference here is to difference growing out of the fecund soil of personal awareness and individual need. Individualism emerging out of need to fulfill one's own potentialities, regardless of disdain by the mass, can be as powerful as the plant emerging from the seed encased in the concrete roadway.

The herd always travels at the pace of its slowest member; it may send out advance and rear guards, but even they must not be too far from the mass to render required service to the herd. But the pace of the total herd — guards and mass — is set by the slowest member. If not, it ceases to be a herd and becomes a grouping of stragglers, prey to the tracking enemy. This is true of all masses, and of all people when they become enmassed. When that happens to people, who is our tracking enemy to which we can fall prey?

It would seem that the enemy is enmassment and the constant abrasive action that smoothes us into the slickness of absorption into the mass, there to become diluted beyond our own recognition. These grinding factors may be different for each of us, because we may start out with different degrees of roughness and hardness, but what emerges from the tumbler consists far more of similarities than differences.

The morality of a grinding technical society can be nothing but a herd-morality, a mass-morality, functioning at the broadest and shallowest concept acceptable for the herd.

We have rather a clear example of this in space-science and in the current moon-mania affecting governments. Our nation is planning to spend eight to ten billion dollars in preliminary attempts to send an American to the moon and bring him back. This expenditure is only for the next five years or less. It is estimated that the expenditure will reach some thirty billion dollars before the actual moon-shot is attempted. By comparison, the Manhattan Project, which hastened the nuclear age, cost two billion dollars. Our government's basic argument for the need for this enormous national exertion was thus stated by the President: "No single space-project in this period will be more impressive to mankind or more important for the long-range exploration of space."

There is something indecent and immoral in the whole concept of our capturing the moon in order to impress mankind and, by implication, demonstrating to the world our superiority in satellite weaponry. Will man's grasp of his environment expand and deepen if one country races another to the moon? Perhaps, if this project were some sort of Olympic Space Meet, with all contestants retaining their amateur standing, as it were.

Of course, a moon-landing would be impressive; and, if we survive, it will at some point in time unquestionably become fact. However, an attempt on the part of any nation to reach the moon for purposes of prestige falls far short of being impressive. If reaching the moon and returning to Earth is a great opportunity for mankind, the project and the attempt present an even greater opportunity for mankind to demonstrate and strengthen the unity of all nations and peoples.

Our government could demonstrate its morality and high purpose by calling upon all nations to participate in this project. Certainly such world-participation poses enormous problems; but not nearly as enormous as the moon-project itself. If we can more easily solve the vaster problems of the project while remaining incapable of solving the problems of world-participation in the project, the results, no matter how successful, will generate distortion and imbalance.

The world-participation in the International Geophysical Year is still generating benefits accruing to all mankind. Why cannot an International Geophysical Year expand into an International Lunar Decade?

For any single government, no matter how rich in resources, to exert itself to the extent needed for this enormous moon-project, and to exclude the participation and resources from the remaining peoples of the world is wasteful, arrogant, and immoral, precisely because such exclusion will generate distortion and imbalance.

In this context, the mass-morality of government in its stated attempt to benefit mankind with its moon-shot is synonymous with mass-immorality toward the mankind it seeks to impress.

Morality can be only an individual concept and an individual strength. To achieve and maintain an individual morality requires a personal exertion beyond that required for the mass. And since every organism must be able to recuperate from whatever exertion it expends, recuperation itself assumes a deeper significance.

If recuperation, especially from nonmaterial exertion, becomes complex to the point of near-impossibility, anxiety and torsion will inevitably deepen and spread. There is an absolute direct relationship between these two factors, which has been known scientifically for many years. On all levels of human relations individual torsion is rising at such an accelerated rate that anxiety has become a grave national symptom, and an increasing burden the weight of which we all share in one way or another. Corrective measures that ignore, or actually misunderstand, the nature of recuperation can be, at best, only a delaying action.

French physicians have experimented with what they call deep-sleep medicine. The patient is placed under heavy sedation, chilled in ice, and brought into a low-temperature room. Body temperature, respiration, and metabolism are drastically reduced; the patient, fed intravenously, is maintained in a near-comatose condition for up to 72 hours, and then gradually brought back to normal body function. The intention is to permit the patient to recuperate from his mental and emotional exertions through a form of medically induced hibernation. However, the patient soon becomes addicted to this induced hibernation, which becomes less and less effective for him. People are not hummingbirds; recuperative processes effective for one organism are rarely suitable for another.

The huge quantities of sleeping pills and tranquilizers taken so matter-of-factly by so many people are attempts to induce a sort of hibernation, a removal from reality. These external inducements probably have medical value, but they are scarcely suitable for a way of life.

There are many obvious biologic functions that are purely individual, that nobody can do for anybody else, that cannot be borrowed, purchased, or acquired by force. There are other biologic functions that are not so obviously individual.

Recuperation is one of these functions, perhaps not so obviously individual, affecting every factor — biologic and nonbiologic — of man's existence.

Man is a constant modifier of himself and his environment, continually risking through ignorance or avarice his ability to survive.

What would it avail us to construct a smoothly automatic and mechanistic world if it can be utilized only by smoothly automatic and mechanistic people?

Can we extricate ourselves from the grinding tumbler before we become so slicked that nothing adheres to us — or we to anything else — but are rolled by every erratic current that comes along?

At the very least, the search for personal extrication becomes a search for personal value and individual freedom. These can neither be purchased nor borrowed; and nobody can seek them for anyone but himself.

(July 14, 1961)

VI

The Fat of the Land

BIO-ECOLOGY RECOGNIZES THREE basic requirements for the
continued existence of all organisms. They must have nourishment; they must be able to recuperate from whatever
exertions they expend; and they must be able to reproduce
in order that the species may continue to exist. When applied
to the Ecology of Man — the inter-relationship of man as a
total organism with his total environment — these life neces-
sities intimately involved with continuously changing social,
political, technological, and especially with economic inter-
relationships assume deeper significance.

It may emerge that advances in society dilute these basic
factors — to the actual weakening of man — particularly
when technological advances are hurriedly translated into
immediate economic gain.

[81]

Nourishment here refers to the physical nourishment of the human organism. It is the contention here that technical advances, essentially because of the subversion of knowledge and its quest, do not necessarily result in advances for bodily nourishment.

Man either by design or through trial and error has always in the past nourished himself to the best of his knowledge. The Mosaic dietary code of the Hebrews of Antiquity, the civilized nutrition of ancient China, the black-soup of Sparta, are all part of the historic nutritional alertness of mankind. Especially in our country, contemporary man's nutritional knowledge is in many ways being used to subvert his health. The primary purpose of this basic requirement for the continued existence of the species has become diluted; and it, as well as the other requirements of recuperation and reproduction, is steadily being seduced by all sorts of nonsensical manipulations.

We have amassed considerable technical data regarding soil, crop, animal, and human nutrition; but in the haste to translate this knowledge into economic gain we have encouraged confusion, weakened our strength before the world, and helped create a national maladjustment of deep and intimate significance. This maladjustment reaches from the producers of our nutritional ingredients, through the processors whose basic interest is economic gain, to the consumers whose basic interest is nourishment for survival.

Actuarial experts maintain that 50 million Americans, approximately one out of every four persons in our country, suffer from obesity (a condition where the body weight is 15 percent or more above a norm determined through statistical evaluation of tables compiled by various insurance companies that have financial interests in the continued health of their premium-paying policy-holders).

That 25 percent of the population of this wealthiest of food-nations suffers from overeating, which is actually a malnutrition-disease, in the face of present and increasing world hunger, is not only immoral but obscene. Most of our food industry caters to this immorality and pampers this obscenity.

If overeating is a symptom of personal uncertainty, as many researchers believe, then obesity is a national physical and mental health problem directly affecting, in some measure, 25 percent of the population. This is of epidemic proportions; and we seem unable to stem its spread.

Those agri-business complexes whose existence is based upon the spread and intensification of this disease are certainly not functioning for the national interest; quite to the contrary. If it were possible, they should be held to account. Such action, of course, would eliminate the lush food advertisements from television, slick magazines, and Sunday supplements — certainly a palatable change.

Historically, man's need for sweets directed him to the wild fruits which contained so many necessary ingredients for his nourishment. Today, this need is used to seduce people into fattening both themselves and the coffers of the sweet food-and-drink industry. Coca-Cola in 1960 had gross sales in excess of $500 million, and a net income of almost $40 million. The gross sales and profits of the franchise and sub-dealers are something else again.

Most animals prefer sweets; and even a cow can be seduced into preferring low-grade straw to rich alfalfa if molasses or ordinary sugar is spread over the straw. However, if a livestockman fed his animals with the same disregard to nourishment that we apply to ourselves, he would soon cease to be a livestockman.

Since obesity is an aspect of malnutrition, it can therefore be said that 25 percent of Americans are malnourished.

The wealth of our land continues to produce a lush harvest of confusion to our national planners, and no solution is on the horizon. The enforced demands we place upon our food-producing acres, continually augmented by our technical advances, greatly increase yields per acre while simultaneously eroding our relationship to the earth and our understanding of its purpose.

The nourishment we must all have for survival comes to us basically from the land; and each producing acre is, in a measurable degree, intimately related to our own survival. The relative ease of storage and transport we now possess spreads this relationship to acres far beyond any geographic borders.

We possess a stockpiled surplus of wheat sufficient for our needs for two-and-a-half years. However, as a result of our technical expenditures and advances, we continually add to this stockpile, even as the older wheat in the pile gradually deteriorates. We may become inured to this anachronism until crop failures in China, for example, magnify the physical and moral problems of our confusion. Here is a direct example of the inter-relationship of nourishment with political policy, and of the wealth of the land with poverty of planning. This is, of course, a complex problem involving all sorts of national and international nuances. Most inter-relationships are complex; but many can be explored and evaluated.

Parenthetically, during late 1960 and early 1961 China purchased vast quantities of surplus grains from Canada and Australia. During the first months of 1961 so many freighters were diverted to the China grain trade that general cargo rates for the remaining sea transport to all countries were increased by some five percent. Had there been a normal grain flow, perhaps general cargo rates could have remained at prior levels.

Periodically, various regulatory plans emerge from government in an attempt to stem the flow of confusion surrounding nourishment. Because we lack a design-theory toward our nourishment-producing earth, these plans are piecemeal and uncoordinated. We seem to consider food a vehicle for the acquisition of wealth; and we sanction some rather disreputable methods in its preparation and enticement.

The vast land-mass of America, at one time a challenge to man in his eternal translation of the richness of the land into human use, has become a challenge for increasingly intricate technology to translate this richness into dollar-acquisition instead of human benefit. We are a relatively new country, yet we already have too much used-up land. Increasingly we mine our farms until their profit capacity has been exhausted; and then we move on to newer areas. But no land is limitless. So much of our country first felt man's acceleration through his machines. In our hasty and unexplored exchange of machine for man, we have lost something irreplaceable from our heritage. We had no period of transition between exploring and exploiting in which to evolve any sort of conceptual approach to the richness of our land; and there now seems to be an impersonal and barren relationship between the people and the life-supporting earth.

We like to think of our country as the wealthiest of food-nations, a living prophesy of continuing plenty. Yet we have no philosophy of agriculture from which we might reap guidance toward the wealth of our land. What we have are weeds of indecision fertilized by avarice. Their harvest is confusion affecting all people, farming and nonfarming, throughout the world.

It has become politically acceptable to state that the farm problem in America is too complex for solution; that we should simply adapt ourselves to live with it; that the earth is really too complicated by human and physical vagaries; that we should therefore devote our energies to a really concerted effort to reach the moon.

The complexity of the farm problem stems basically from our undefined concept of what the land means to us. We must attempt to define, as clearly as we can, the nature of our relationship to the land; and we must evaluate the purpose of bigness. We surely must recognize that bigness does not mean greatness.

While many of the changes created in food processing are unquestionably beneficial, especially in terms of storage and handling, others are not. Actually, the competitive nature of the entire food growing-and-processing complex generates ignorance and confusion. Either by design or by accident, thousands of additives are now part of the American diet, and government is attempting to charge industry with the responsibility of proving the harmlessness of these additives.

The paper industry has some 400 chemicals that go into food containers; the adhesive industry has some 700 such chemicals; some 500 chemicals are used in various rubber products that come in contact with food during the processing cycle; more than 700 chemicals are used to alter flavor, color, and texture, and to retard spoilage — it is a lengthy list. Under present regulatory attempts, the users of these chemicals must test them to assure that they are harmless; then, through the Pure Food and Drug Administration, the United States Government must grant clearance for them to become part of the nourishment of the human organism.

Industry correctly maintains that the cost of proving the harmlessness of its food additives may mount into the millions of dollars. The implication is that additives should be removed only after they prove harmful to the consumer. A spokesman for one of the largest chemical combines in the country complained that the recently attempted safety testings have slowed the pace of research efforts throughout industry.

It is quite impossible, of course, for anyone in this country to purchase a day's food supply without bringing home various numbers and quantities of unproven additives. The implication here is not that additives are automatically harmful, but that our gross ignorance of many of them — an ignorance likely to spread as processing increases, urged by our misdirected fervor for instant everything — is definitely harmful.

This entire situation is primarily brought about by our haste to funnel technical advances into economic gain. During wartime, when all governments restricted their national diets to balanced essentials, the health of their populations showed considerable improvement as long as the essentials were available. Can we, then, not live in peace without destroying our physical well-being in terms of nourishment?

At one time man had time to find out, to transmit knowledge, to explore benefit or harm regarding his basic requirements, and to refine these requirements toward his comfort. Today, in our hasty search for advertised ease in meeting these basic requirements, each technical modification is crowded out by a newer modification, and this, in turn, by another. We depend upon our technicians to guide us when they, themselves, are whipped by the same haste.

It is an historic fact that the so-called peasant cultures developed, through trial and error over generations of time, a nutritive knowledge that later technicians needed only to refine. Many people can remember a time when beef liver, for example, was thrown to the cat. Today it is one of our more expensive meats. The borsch and putcha of Central Europe, and the turnip greens of our own South have all been markers on the road to better nutrition. Even today, jicaro, the apple-sized fruit of a weed of the Central American Indians, points a way to better nutritional balance. For centuries Indian mothers of Central America have eaten jicaro to improve their nursing ability. One day, when we have refined

our knowledge of jicaro, it may possibly become a standard
ingredient in the diet of nursing mothers. This sort of thing
has happened too many times in the past for it to be an
accident of nature. Nature does not make accidents; man
does.

Perhaps our absolute dependence upon nourishment for
survival, along with our ignorance about it, encourages its
manipulation. If a business organization could frighten or
seduce only one percent of the American people to spend only
one penny per day for its newly rediscovered snake-oil Vitamin Q-square, it would gross seven million dollars a year. This
is a tempting morsel to those who manipulate our basic need
for nourishment. There is a marked similarity between the
entire food industry and the Detroit Syndrome. Neither
really considers human need. We need the 300-hp monsters
that glut our highways about as much as we need the food
enticements that glut our digestive systems. Both contribute
to a distortion of the value of the individual.

While a great deal has been written about obesity and
the health and welfare of the individual, little has been said
of how this excess storage of fat affects the economic, social,
and moral well-being of all people. A fantastic percentage
of our wealth is devoted to fattening people, and an equally
fantastic percentage of wealth is devoted to slimming them
down again. This sort of senseless torsion generates all sorts
of cultisms and faddisms, which also drain our national
strength and stamina.

The fat person consumes 1,000 Calories or more per day
in excess of his needs. In terms of beef — which is used here
only as a basic measure — the fat person consumes the equivalent of approximately an additional pound of meat per day
in excess of his needs.

If the experts are correct that 50 million people in our
country suffer from obesity, we therefore need to raise an

additional 50 million pounds of meat per day. Since the average steer on the hoof weighs around 1,000 lbs — of which approximately half is consumed meat — we have to raise an additional 100 million pounds of livestock, equivalent to 100,000 extra head of steers every day.

The yearly cost of obesity to the nation, using beef as the example, is around 36 million head of cattle out of a total cattle population of around 100 million. Obesity, therefore, claims some 36 percent of the total national herd. Millions of acres, more than the total acreage of most of our States, are taken out of planned production to support the fat of the land.

More than a million cattle truckloads a year — if placed bumper-to-bumper they would stretch 8,000 miles — are required to carry these excess Calories.

It can be figured mathematically that there are thousands of pharmaceutical and equipment firms, fertilizer and insecticide companies, salesmen, supermarkets, garbage collectors, paper manufacturers — people in every phase of industry — whose full time is allocated to obesity.

There are many other measures by which to gauge this cost. The people of India, for example, consume less than 2,000 Calories a day, on an average. The fat people in America can actually feed 25 million Indians a day, while still retaining for themselves a daily consumption of more than 3,000 Calories. In this regard it is pertinent to remember that most of the world still suffers from continuing hunger. More than 75 percent of the men, women, and children of the world will go to bed hungry tonight. It was so last night, and will be so tomorrow night. The term "hunger" is not used to mean the complete absence of food and the resultant fairly rapid death from famine. It is used to mean the lack of the forty or so food constituents needed to maintain health, and to the resultant malnutrition and its attendant diseases. More than half of the world's population lives on the verge of actual and continuing hunger, while another quarter of the world's population is constantly undernourished. Despite technical progress, more and more people are increasingly hungry.

While it is difficult to arrive at medical costs caused or aggravated by obesity, medical opinion is unanimous in declaring that excess fat contributes heavily to our national health costs. The numbers of beds in crowded hospitals occupied by patients whose ailments are aggravated by obesity is a matter of conjecture, but certainly the cost in terms of doctors, nurses, pharmacists, laboratory technicians is fantastic.

Our surplus economy may not dictate that we tighten our belts. Our morality, however, does dictate that we do not loosen them.

In weight-conscious America, Calorie counting is something of a national pastime. (A Calorie is the amount of heat required to raise the temperature of one kilogram of water — approximately one quart — one degree centigrade at atmospheric pressure. The British Thermal Unit or BTU, is the amount of heat required to raise the temperature of one pound of water one degree Fahrenheit at or near its point of maximum density. Approximately four BTU's equal one Calorie.)

Actually, as a guide and measure of food value the calorie is generally meaningless since it is a measure of gross energy, and not of nutritional value. This measure-limitation of the calorie should be recognized.

In determining the caloric value of food, we calculate the weight, in grams, of the fat, carbohydrate, and protein contained in one pound — equivalent to 454 grams — of that food. We then multiply the fat grams by approximately 9.0, the carbohydrate and protein grams by approximately 4.0, and add the total, which is then recognized as the number of Calories present in one pound of that particular food.

The types of fat, carbohydrate, or protein of the particular food, and whether these fractions are digested by the body or pass through unused, are not taken into account when compiling Calorie, or gross-energy, factors.

Net-energy values, however, are something else. Net energy is the gross or Calorie energy contained in a substance ingested by an organism, minus the energy lost in feces, urine, combustible gases and heat increment. This factor is expressed as Thermal Net Energy, or TNE.

The TNE factor of the identical ingredient differs for different species. For example, the TNE of the same corn is different for hogs than for cattle. For years, Mid-west livestockmen have run one hog with each ten steers they plan to fatten on corn. The cattle are fed; the hog is not. Yet the corn that passes through the steers, only partially digested, is sufficient to fatten the hog.

The TNE factor of the identical ingredient also differs for different animals within the same species. For instance, the Holstein cow and the smaller Jersey extract different quantities of net energy from the same alfalfa.

Even for the same organism, human or animal, net-energy factors of the identical ingredients differ under different conditions. Underfeeding, for example, alters the TNE, as does overfeeding; the age and condition of health of the animal ingesting the ingredient is of great importance in net-energy evaluations. Climatic conditions also have their effects. Combinations of ingredients alter the TNE factors of each of the ingredients, as do additives. The more complex the organism, the more complex are the inter-relationships of the TNE factors.

It is now gradually being recognized that patients who assure their physicians that they have not fudged on their diets, but do not have the anticipated weight loss, may be telling the truth. Their net-energy conversion factors may be greater than expected. Some advanced researchers in the study of saturated and unsaturated fat-relationships to heart disease may find that TNE factors in human nutrition play a highly significant role because of their complex variability within the individual.

The determination of net energy is one of the most involved and most costly procedures in animal nutrition. This is so because of the various interrelationships that must be considered. The TNE factors we use today are only approximations; and for many ingredients we do not have even approximations.

We know a great deal more of the Total Digestible Nutrients (TDN) and Thermal Net Energy factors in animal feeding than we do in human feeding. We possess more overall knowledge of animal nutrition than we do of human nutrition. Animals are, of course, easier to manipulate in this sort of experimentation. Laboratory rats and even cows can be kept in net-energy control rooms for days and months for data accumulation, while this sort of laboratory regimen is extremely complicated with humans. Furthermore, the economic gain from proper animal nutrition and experimentation is clearly evident to livestockmen and the feed industry. Economic gain is not as clearly evident toward humans.

In the light of new techniques, we need a great deal more knowledge about our basic requirements. Research programs in human net-energy determinations could well be sponsored by governments, universities, and foundations, but hardly by industry, since industry here has a special interest that makes it suspect. The canning-sugar industries, for instance, would have some sales difficulty if consumers realized that fruits canned in heavy syrup have seven teaspoonfuls of sugar to every cup of fruit, in addition to numerous other additives.

The label on the can now merely states that the fruit is packed in heavy syrup.

Of course, all prepared foods and feeds must be labeled by law; but the current utterly inadequate labeling presents a false sense of assurance. We purchase most of our nourishment with misdirected faith.

Livestock feeds are tagged with a percentage listing of the protein, fat, fibre, and ash content of the mixed ingredients. This listing is slightly informative, but details little of the actual value of the feeds. Attempts to add to the label information of greater importance — such as Total Digestible Nutrients, Vitamin A content, and so on — have always been strongly resisted by the agricultural industry. Animals in our country continue to be generally better fed than humans.

We do not have a proper unit of measurement for human value, especially regarding the basic requirements needed for the continued existence of the species. Certainly grams, pounds, or tons are valid measures, but not for distance; nor do metres, feet, or miles measure weight. In terms of human value, must we be limited to economic gain as the universal measure? It scarcely makes any sort of sense.

If progress demands that technological advances be hurriedly translated into economic gain regarding a factor as basic as nourishment, perhaps progress itself is mislabeled, and should be exposed to more penetrating public scrutiny.

(March 10, 1961)

VII

Technobiologic Reproducers

IN ALL OF nature only those biologic organisms survive that partake of gradual modification processes. The exception to this rule are the mutations, those suddenly produced variations about which we know very little.

Nonbiological changes in nature, however, often occur with speed and violence, and occasionally with drastic effects — as with the Polar colds that swooped down over much of Earth. When such changes occur, organisms must accelerate the gradualness of their modification processes in order to survive in their altered environment — or perish. Natural terminal sequences occurred many times in the past; and science continues to uncover fossil-evidence of species and genera that were, for one reason or another, extinguished.

It is the contention here that we are living in an environment which has been drastically altered within one generation, and that the gradualness of mankind's modification-
processes is being accelerated to a near point of turbulence.

Technobiologic modifications are converting man from
Homo sapiens — man regarded as an organic species — into
Homo atomicus — which may be man regarded as a contrived
series of separations, converted by his own redesign into a
species different from what he was even one generation ago.
We seem to be subjected with increasing intensity and ingenuity to technobiologic modifications whose obvious symptoms are presented in the ascendant diseases to which man
becomes prey as his society accelerates: colitis, paranoia,
schizophrenia, and other manifestations of anxiety toward an
environment he does not comprehend, and toward which, in
the midst of the material plenty he seeks with such urgency,
he seems to be in inarticulate rebellion.

The concept that anything man does is natural for him
has been used throughout history to absolve him of his inhumanity and to justify many of his deeds conceived in ignorance and executed with abandon toward himself and his total
environment.

Man continues to demonstrate that he is the least organized and most destructive organism in nature; the wildest
animal, capable of taming all other animals but himself; the
universal solvent that cannot be contained. Since he can
provoke change for nonnatural gain, man is the species least
directed by natural evolutionary processes.

Evolution is, of course, a gradual process with minute
changes which are undetectable until they reach a point of
recognition. What gradual evolutionary processes are taking
place at this moment in man's time on Earth? Is his seat
spreading because of too much sitting and are his arches
failing because of too little walking? Is this body ailing be-

cause of dependence upon wondrous pill products and is his spirit failing because only his mechanical extensions soar?

Since his beginnings, man has always modified his ecology. The fact of his existence is his single greatest environmental modifier. As he becomes more skillful in manipulating nature, the modifications he makes are often drastic and violent, and occasionally self-destructive.

Multilane super highways do not, of themselves, assure the traveler's safe passage and arrival. Because of their mechanized hypnosis, such highways frequently hasten the terminal accident.

We are becoming increasingly similar to the aircraft on the take-off runway; its passenger list full; its equipment mechanically certified; its engines leashed and ready to hurl it skyward; its distant point of arrival hopefully clear. But its present point of departure is rapidly being closed-in by impenetrable fog, and it cannot take off. And there it waits with muted rumblings — a big beautiful man-spawned accomplishment, enveloping its anxious passengers and skillful crew in glistening metallic sheath, product of trained technicians. When clearance is refused by the tower-dispatcher, it returns to the loading apron to disembark the disturbed passengers who purchased their flight in good faith, but who are forced to remain Earth-bound until visibility improves. Even the wings of the aircraft seem to droop.

Our point of departure is enshrouded with nebulous promise. Our hoped-for point of personal arrival is distant and unclear. Encased in our glistening mechanically certified devices we wait — for what? For some tower-dispatcher, surrounded by still other devices and gadgetry, to issue clearance for our personal flight — or to command our return to the waiting room, there to remain keyed-up to whatever expectations may emerge from electronic speakers to direct our lives?

But dispatchers and their mechanical extensions can govern only the mechanical extensions of man. Man himself cannot be so governed unless he relinquishes his personal sovereignty by permitting himself to respond as a mechanical extension — subservient to devices or to manipulators of devices who are perhaps more skillful than he is, but who are actually also mechanized. Unhappily, this is precisely what is emerging from the accelerated technobiologic modification-processes toward which mankind, all over the world, seems to be yearning. Boastfully we envelop ourselves in a glistening metallic skin; and when the reflected light of personal doubt or inquiry blinds us, we think ourselves bejeweled. We are only bewitched and bewildered .

Our drastically altered ecology, with its accelerated technobiologic modification processes, has been brought about in one generation by the mainly abortive emergences of applied science and technology which we accept in our country as part of our mechanical heritage, and for which the people of the world seem to clamor as a tangible indication of their emerging statures. This alteration is considerably more basic than the external manifestations of material goods and services that ease man through his life-span.

The reference is neither to weaponry nor to other examples of auto-intoxication resulting from a world in ferment. The reference here is simply to reproduction — one of the three basic requirements for the continued survival of any organism. The other two basic requirements are nourishment and recuperation.

The contention here is that man's conceptual attitudes toward reproduction are being altered — not only through genetic malfunction, but through irreversible changes in his environment.

For a biologic organism reproduction involves merely the continuation of the species, usually with imperceptible changes occurring from generation to generation. Even such gradual modifications have not always resulted in the improvement of the species; occasionally they have brought about attrition and gradual weakening of the species until it was extinguished.

Historically, reproduction for man was simply biologic. Then, in his implacable thrust toward civilization, reproduction became of political–military importance, as witnessed by the government drives for more birthings instituted by Mussolini and Hitler only a generation ago. Soon after the extermination of these two centers of world infection, reproduction assumed economic significance, as witnessed by government drives for less birthings instituted in Japan, India, and Scandinavia, presently observed by an anxious world so rapidly becoming crowded.

Today, human reproduction throughout the world is assuming scientific significance. The reasons are numerous and varied. Population-pressures confronting diminishing Earth-resources is one reason; another is the population-increase in the so-called "inept strata" threatening to lower the stature of our society; still another is the fact that masses of people are no longer needed to wrest sustenance from the Earth. Our mechanical extensions have released mankind from animal-toil, and the greater the number of people who share in the spoils of progress, the less will be the individual's share. This factor is of direct concern to the emerging nations of Africa and Asia who fear their technologic progress will be unable to keep pace with their rapidly increasing populations.

Basic to the scientific concern with reproduction is the random nature of impregnation. Science, and particularly technology, strives for mechanical perfection through design. The biologic fact that any random male and female of proper age and physical capacity can propagate the species is anathema to science and technology.

LEWIS AND CLARK COLLEGE LIBRARY
PORTLAND, OREGON 97219

Certainly a highly articulate plea can be made for bringing to bear the full weight of science on this basic requirement for the continued survival of the species.

For man, reproduction involves far more than the biologic factors of impregnation, gestation, and parturition. Today, factors of design can drastically modify both impregnation and gestation.

All sorts of skillful reproductive techniques have been developed during the past generation in many parts of the world. Early in 1961 at Cambridge University, British animal-research scientists successfully removed eight fertilized ova from a ewe and transplanted them into a live rabbit for incubation during a flight to South Africa. On arrival at their destination, the transplants were transferred into ewes of a local African breed, which later gave them birth. Subsequent experiments indicated that an embryo flock of some forty sheep can be transported in one rabbit incubator. Since the cost of sending such incubators to any part of the world is infinitesimal, this technique probably will become fairly widespread.

Diligent research may certainly find a technique for removing fertilized human ova, transplanting them into an incubator-carrier, and air-shipping them to any part of the world for subsequent transference into a distant human gestator.

Artificial insemination has been a technobiologic fact in the reproduction of cattle for many years. In our country natural dairy-cow fertilization is an increasing biologic rarity. The purpose of artificial insemination in the dairy herd is to improve the breed and to achieve its maximum potentiality; it also eliminates the need to maintain a number of bulls for the herd, along with the attendant problems of proper bull-maintenance. While a good sire-bull may be able to impregnate thirty or forty cows a year naturally, the same bull —

since nature is so very prolific with its seed — can fertilize a thousand or more cows a year through artificial insemination. Furthermore, through artificial insemination, an expensive bull, supposedly containing those genetic characteristics wanted by the livestock owner, can be shared by numerous herds.

The same general thinking is being directed toward human sperm as science strives for perfection through design. Since we possess techniques for the retention of active sperm for many years, why not consider broad artificial insemination for the upgrading of the human breed?

Of course, the pure-breed cattle owner who builds his hopes and his fortune upon the foundations of classic genetics, by out-breeding undesirable characteristics and in-breeding desirable ones, is faced with the dilemma of reaching the mountaintop where he must remain, unable to come down, isolated by his own drive for purity of breed. His search for a bull capable of continuing the upgrading of his herd consumes him and his fortune. He is mathematically certain to reach a point where, for him, no such animal exists. When they near this point, astute livestockmen disperse their herds through sale or exchange, beget a new, lower-graded herd, and start the climb all over again. Obsession with purity is a denial of nature, which is in itself a blending.

Science, however, is not nearly as obsessed with purity as it is with perfection through design. Perfection and design must have purpose and design-theory; and today's science cannot, as yet, even begin to assess man's purpose in the universe since it has, as yet, no design-theory toward Man on Earth.

A Nobel Laureate and geneticist seriously proposed a project for the collection and storage of sperm from the so-called "great men" of our time. After these men have been dead for some twenty-five years, their lives and works would then be evaluated and, if found still worthy by the evaluation board, their living sperm would be reactivated and used for the artificial insemination of properly chosen female receivers. The 25-year period was chosen to allow time for an objective evaluation of the great men's lives and works, and in order to wait for one generation-cycle to remove the personal aspect.

Such seminal preservation is certainly technically feasible and aesthetically acceptable. We accept blood banks, eye banks, and other visceral depositories as being of great medical value. Acceptance, with glory, by the second generation receivers of such artificial insemination poses no difficulty to a science becoming so increasingly skillful in merchandising its contributions to the progress of man.

Of course, since the evaluation board would become a collective foster father, as it were, to tens of thousands, it would have not only a grave responsibility but a rather monumental problem. What measurement of value would its members use? Some physical and intellectual specifications would have to be accepted. A person suffering from deafness would surely not be acceptable — which would have eliminated Beethoven. A person suffering from heresy toward his age could certainly not be safe to include, thus eliminating Galileo and many others.

Perhaps an evaluation of the board's specifications would indicate that, despite artificial insemination dilutions and techniques, there simply may not be enough available sperm with which to make the rounds.

Truly, the inanities emerging from scientific absurdity are disheartening. The fact that such inanities are technically feasible does not make them less absurd.

For man's continued existence, genetic selectivity is, of course, important — but by whom? In the final analysis, no human being is capable of self-selectivity. The problem is one of principles. What principles are we to employ in determining the values of the different qualities of the individual? Of the qualities we may wish to strengthen genetically? And of the qualities we may wish to eliminate genetically? Even a published list of principles, compiled by an international board of leading evaluators, would have little meaning, since no individual can judge himself with objectivity. If the individual is then to be judged by a board, who then judges the individual members of the board?

The point here is that no man-made system of values can have any sort of final judgment regarding man, who is capable of taming all other animals but himself. If tameness means domestication, then to whom is man domesticated? The domesticated animal is subservient to the will of the master. Who is the master of man? He has no master but himself. He continues to traverse an uncontained path through all of nature. He remains untamed, for who will tame him?

This untamability is the genetic strength of man and, in the final analysis, the guarantor of his personal freedom.

Master-race ideologies, whether of an Aryan or a scientific concept, depend upon the imposition of enforcements or enticements upon subjects until they submit to authority. Gratefully this can not come about so long as man remains untamable and unsystematized. Despite attempts at enforcement, no system of values can, for him, retain its basic requirement of ultimate objectivity. Valid and ultimate objectivity is a universal solvent; therefore, how can it be contained?

Master-computers, regardless of scope and complexity, even if they achieve the size of a continent, cannot of themselves systematize principles of breeding to achieve predetermined values which can then retain any sort of fluidity. The moment values are programmed they become rigid and can function only according to past values, and not according to future unanticipated values that may emerge at the next moment. If we depend upon science to be the master-director for the breeding of man, we depend upon rigidity and upon the rejection of fluidity; we pay obeisance to false gods with little direction and less objectivity, who will continue to lead us astray.

If the aim of science is to better man — whatever that may mean — through selective breeding, science is then concerned with the systematic breeding of tamed animals. For man this is an obvious absurdity, since who will tame the tamers and select the breedings? Ultimately, the selector himself would have to be able to achieve an objectivity outside himself; he would have to be uncontained, untamed, undomesticated, and wild. The only selector meeting these requirements, without the imposition of force or enticement is not individual man, but all of man.

If the purpose of science is to help create an environment in which mankind can hope to achieve its potentialities — whatever they may be — then science should strive to conserve the untrammeled nature of man and his untamability.

This is one of the basic dilemmas of science — which seeks perfection through design — when the only valid design for man is the unsystematic method of nature.

But to science, un-system is anathema; and by its actual striving for perfection — a disease in itself — science constricts man into torsioned and unnatural modifications.

Science cannot assure mankind's continued existence, much less his betterment; it can only guarantee mankind's extinction through the theoretical possibility of total erasure.

Since only those organisms can survive that partake of gradual, random, and unsystematized modification processes, science, when it attempts to accelerate these processes, becomes self-defeating.

Perhaps the ancient proverb of the Khurdustani Devil-worshippers is more to the point: "If God is all-supreme, then why the Devil? . . ." And so they believed in the Eighth Angel whom they worshipped — man himself.

But worship implies obeisance in token of submission, and obeisance implies domestication as the fact of submission. Yet man cannot be domesticated since he is untamable.

Man, therefore, remaining the wildest animal in all of nature, cannot worship — even himself.

(November 8, 1961)

VIII

Orphans from Reason

IN A COMPLEX world that is capable of orphaning itself from reason, man continually seeks a base line of unquestioned personal truth, a segment of universal truth from which he may seek bearings for his one-way passage through space and time; a personal light drawn from an undiminished universal light with which to dispel surrounding darkness. Yet in his search for this universality he continues to stumble, unseeing, over precisely those markers along the path that can point him toward the direction he seeks.

The only least common denominator of human comprehension that is equally valid throughout the world and throughout the entire history of man has always been and continues to be basic science and basic inquiry. All other expressions of human endeavor and aspirations — depending, as they do, upon constantly varying cultural factors for comprehension, pursuit, and acquisition — are essentially regional in space and time.

God is certainly a regional concept; and for hundreds of millions the Bible is a book for Infidels. But in all parts of the world, so recognized since the beginnings of human intellect, two plus two are four in simple arithmetic.

The point here is not whether the sum of two numbers is greater than the concept of God, but that the sum of two numbers is a universal fact whereas God is not a universal concept; and the concepts of even a supreme God change with man's history and with his views of self-righteousness.

The pious torturers of the Holy Inquisition robed themselves in the vestments of a flint-like God who sparked the fires of the stake to which many believers in a less rigid God had been lashed.

When Giordano Bruno was burned at the stake by the Inquisition in 1600 he was certainly guilty of believing in an eternal God different from the eternal God of the Christianity of that time. He had rejected the rigid astronomy of Aristotle, which made the Earth the center of the universe, and espoused the fluid theories of Copernicus, which allowed for the possibility of innumerable worlds in the universe. Bruno publicly believed that amid all the varying phenomena of the universe there was one unifying immeasurability which lent coherence to all phenomena. This, to Bruno, was God: the universal unifying substance from which all things of necessity come, a God whose manifestation was in an infinite and animated universe, but a universe so vast and so difficult to comprehend that it gave no true knowledge of an infinitely remote God. To Giordano Bruno, man's highest function was the contemplation of the divine unity, and man's destiny was immortality as a part of this divine unity.

Precisely such beliefs whipped around him the flames of the Holy Inquisition; and his arrogance, recorded in history, did not endear him to those who so rigidly guarded or, perhaps, imprisoned their God with fire and with the threat of eternal damnation.

And so Giordano Bruno, in 1600, was burned for his arrogance and his heresies; but in 1898 a statue to him was unveiled in Rome's Campo dei Fiori, the place of his incineration. Today Bruno's somewhat primitive pantheism has become quite respectable, and Bruno's God is today more acceptable than the God of the Inquisitors.

Which Christianity was universal? Bruno's? His Inquisitors'? Or neither? And what of the Supreme God of other beliefs and other aspirations?

However, a basic truth, once expressed, is not at all regional in terms of space and time. It is quite likely that the universality of basic science and basic inquiry remains the staunchest hope for the future of mankind.

Basic science is a search for principles and not for applications. Principles can become beacons to guide us along the path, while applications can frequently blind us so that we stumble over ourselves and our neighbors.

All principles, scientific and nonscientific, can emerge only from individual awareness and individual exhilaration and freedom, while applications emerge mainly from group-activities and reflect group restrictions. Applications frequently dilute and contort principles to a point where the principles themselves become rigid with encrustations. Those who practice encrusted science become readily corruptible since they mistake shadow for substance and acclaim for accomplishment. Manifestations of science must be paid for; and many in the world who cannot pay are then seduced into all sorts of enslavements in order to acquire these manifestations. Principles no longer seem to have value by themselves. Even an idea seems to have merit only if it is translatable into some sort of application.

It has become one of the delusions of science that if a scientist is to make any sort of major contribution he must do so before he is thirty since, after that age, like the professional athlete, he is on the downward path of his capabilities. So many young scientists expend themselves on one main project that has some chance of being successful that they grow aged and fatigued prior to maturity. Should his project succeed, the young scientist is promptly encrusted with all sorts of problems involved in translating his promise into application. It is precisely in this area of application that the promise of the scientist is diverted and his creativity diluted.

However, if the individual refuses to allow the encrustations of living to render him rigid or its scouring tides to gouge deep trenches that imprison his mind and spirit and restrict his horizons, his creativity frequently increases with his years. The simultaneous expansion of years and creativity is especially true in literature, music, art, and in those aspects of science that are individual pursuits and not group activities.

Manipulation of principles in the accelerated search for application by nations and organizational complexes has not only sheathed science with glitter; it has also generated worldwide personal and emotional disturbances within the body of science itself. Aside from any direct relationship to international warfare, many valid examples of this manipulation of principles are happening throughout the entire spectrum of science.

Automation, that symbol of technologic application and electronic promise of material plenty for all, presents many of the aspects of conflict. Automation has become a deep personal disturbance to workers displaced by machines. Demanding uniformity and conformity, it is in constant conflict with principles and individual freedom. Also, automation can spew forth vaster quantities of goods than can be utilized; therefore, in order to keep automated complexes functioning, designed obsolescence automatically becomes a factor of automation; and designed obsolescence implies the acceptance of planned termination or suicide as a way of life. Automation carries more threat than promise for mankind, although this need not be. But we know very little of the ecology of automation, of its inter-relationship with an environment it so drastically modifies.

Chemistry, joined to medicine, presents other aspects of the conflict between application and principle. Certainly the plethora of pills to tranquilize the mind hinders the basic scientific comprehension of the mind. Chemical euphoria, in supplying a sense of well-being and buoyancy, may smoothly encrust conflict but can scarcely resolve it.

In the early days of the Industrial Revolution in England, a similar type of euphoria emerged from casks of readily available and low-cost gin, without which the people would not have accepted their machine-made misery and the cruel conditions of their existence.

The medical practitioner, daily buffeted by an increasingly complex whirl of ailments about which he needs to know considerably more than he does, too frequently accepts easy assistance from the plethora of drugs flowing so irresistibly toward him from the pill-presses of the pharmaceutical industry. And medical practice, encouraging the haste of the drug companies to make the best-seller lists with their scientific-sounding product-names, is increasingly governed by trial-and-error.

Medicine has made huge strides in recent years, but these strides have been made by very few in a field crowded by very many who accept the glory and profits and offer little in return.

The great principles of bacteriology and immunology that emerged from the unfettered minds of Pasteur and his colleagues certainly helped generate the population dilemma in which the world now finds itself. Actually, very little basic

scientific inqury has been devoted to the problems of population-pressures. We do not even know, with any certainty, the
extent of the problem. And the only direction toward solution seems to be more birth-control pills to restrict the numbers of people.

Too frequently, the application of principles emerging
from basic science and basic inquiry does not benefit man
but only clutters his progress and contorts him into a departure from reality.

The conflicts between application and principle within
the nuclear dilemma are immense. An atomic energy power-
generating plant for peaceful purposes is impossible for any
country engaged in preparations for war because such power,
coursing through regional and national grids, is used directly
or indirectly by the military–industrial complexes. Even
disregarding this aspect of the problem, an atomic energy
plant constructed along the coast in order to utilize sea-water
for cooling purposes generates all sorts of other problems.
Sea-water discharged into the ocean from power-generating
plants would be considerably warmer than the surrounding
sea; warm salt-water is toxic to much of marine life, and a
single atomic energy power plant can generate extensive
damage and imbalance in vast volumes of the sea. We know
very little of such inter-relationships, yet we hoist such plans
as self-congratulatory banners only to be rapidly shredded by
the as yet uncontrolled gusts of world awareness.

An elder scientist who helped conceive the original nuclear
weaponry project has seriously proposed a retaliatory principle for the leashing of his beast. This pre-atomic-age scientist's thoughtful suggestion was for an exchange of nuclear
weapons technicians between the U.S.A. and the U.S.S.R.
The Russian technicians would live in an underground silo
in a major American city with a thermonuclear missile constantly ready. The American technicians would also live in

an underground silo in a major Russian city with a thermonuclear missile constantly ready. Each group would then be
hostage for the other. Should one country start a thermonuclear war, its en-siloed technicians would retaliate by
destroying the enemy's city and themselves.

Once again the concept emerges that equal fear equally
shared is progress, that the retaliatory principle would im-
mobilize the threat of thermonuclear warfare; that immobility is progress.

While it is not implicit in this proposal — which could be
known as Project Hostage, or Project Tom Sawyer — it could
be assumed that when Red China achieves her thermonuclear
potential, the threat would be eliminated by expanding Project Tom Sawyer; the U.S.A. would have one team of Russian
technicians under one American city and another team of
Red Chinese under another American city; the U.S.S.R.
would also have two teams, American and Chinese, under
two Russian cities; and the Red Chinese would have one team
of Americans and one of Russians — making a total of six
en-siloed world groups, each with its thermonuclear missile
at the ready. Then, when France joins in, there would be at
least twelve such teams in the world, enough for a meet of
Olympic proportions. As other countries achieved thermonuclear potentials — a convenience that applied science and
technology is making cheaper all the time — we could have
hundreds and even thousands of such teams peppered
throughout the world, each with its own colors and boosters
and its own multimegaton idol at the ready. There can be no
question as to the efficacy of such a plan. The building, man-
ning, weaponing, and maintaining of such silos would be
immobilizing — to everything.

This proposal was not made by a little boy with a bean
shooter; it was seriously offered by a serious scientist for
serious consideration in the name of scientific progress, humanity, and freedom of the individual.

A younger post-atomic-age scientist, unwilling to clutter our planet with missiles and radioactivity, seriously proposed that a proper astral body, not too far from Earth to be effective, could be charged with the proper rockets that would, upon a signal from Earth, thrust its astral body out of orbit in such manner that its weight and force would be hurled against an Earth-target where it could easily obliterate half a continent.

This proposal, which could be called Project Heavenly Host, should quite logically have been extended so that two equivalent astral bodies would be so charged: one aimed at the U.S.S.R. and one at the U.S.A. Both bodies would be simultaneously activated by a single gold button in order that one could not be hurled without the other. Here we would really have equal fear equally shared. But not quite ultimate fear ultimately shared — not yet. When Red China achieves her thermonuclear potential another proper astral body would be charged, aimed at Red China and tied into the common triggering system. And when France joins in, still another proper astral body would be charged, targeted, and tied into the common triggering system. As other countries achieved thermonuclear potentials, still other astral bodies would be charged, targeted at the thermonuclear nations, and all tied into the common triggering system. Here we would have ultimate fear ultimately shared; and in the workings of the equation, the world should now have ultimate progress. Will the heavens declare the glories of science and the firmament show its handiwork?

Here again, the results of such projects, presented by scientists who long to be considered responsible individuals fighting for progress and the freedom of the individual, are to achieve immobility. Of course this is not their stated purpose; they maintain that they are seeking to achieve world-balance through a uniformity of threat, hope, and salvation.

This all applies to thermonuclear warfare and to its threat. For chemical and bacteriological warfare these project would need some modification; but not enough to invalidate the slogan, "Progress Through Immobility!"

Of greater significance in the conflict between applications and principles within the nuclear dilemma was the hasty blending of two basically dissimilar ingredients, government and science, each actually antagonistic to the other. Government and science are not at all compatible. All government is based upon applications emerging mainly from group-activities and reflecting group-restrictions. But basic science and basic inquiry can function only when they are unrestricted; and their principles can be uncovered only through individual pursuit.

Political leaders are becoming increasingly dependent upon scientists in order to retain their leadership; and scientists are certainly becoming increasingly more dependent upon governments and industrial complexes for their ability to function and to acquire the expensive tools of the scientific trade. A sort of mutually parasitic relationship exists between government and science, as both feed off the host-body of mankind.

One of America's leading applicators of science to war wrote that "war preparations are necessary in order to justify the deepest human desire for knowledge . . ." and that "society does not accept the desire for knowledge unless it is in some way tied to war . . ."

The implication here is that disarmament would become a scientific disaster; and that an arms race is needed, not for war preparations, but for the survival of science.

Such expanding absurdities result when the universality of basic science and basic inquiry is denied; when science relinquishes its personal awareness, exhilaration, and freedom

to enter into an incestuous relationship with the stepbrother
or stepfather image government, there to become orphaned
from reason.

Yet the sound of science remains rampant throughout
government in a continuous filibuster that has little relationship to reality.

Man has always sought universal concepts of inerasable
value for himself and his world. Actually, there must be at
least one single factor that remains true for the individual
throughout his life as a base line for morality and ethics; and
for mankind throughout its history. This factor could be
good or it could be evil; but it must remain the absolute
factor, unaffected by regionalism.

Killing is not a universal evil. Under certain conditions
people get medals for killing; and certainly various faiths
have used killing as encouragement for straying souls to
return to the fold. A Jesuit spokesman has declared that it
is quite justifiable in the eyes of his God to shoot your neighbor if he tries to break into the nuclear bomb shelter where
you and your family are already secured.

Even Giordano Bruno's God may have had other thoughts
about this.

Stealing is also not a universal evil. Some societies actually encourage it, and honor those practitioners who achieve
expertise.

Lying to someone else is again not a universal evil; even
in high places it is condoned.

Perhaps the single factor that remains unequivocally
evil is intellectual dishonesty to self. Perhaps this is the
base line for all morality and ethics, for all concepts of right
and wrong, good and evil.

In this context, basic science, in attempting to deny its
own universality, has been intellectually dishonest for some
time past.

The incompatible mixture of government and science pollute one another. Why cannot basic science disassociate itself from entangling alliances with governments? Of course, applications of science are necessary adjuncts to governments and industrial complexes as they attempt, often competitively, to translate application into many forms of gain. Basic science is merely tolerated in the anticipation that what emergences from it will be translatable into competitive political and economic gains. Yet all principles and guidance can only emerge from the vigorous pursuit of basic science.

The last paragraph that Einstein wrote was part of a radio and television address he offered to make in 1955 to celebrate the anniversary of Israel's independence. He died with his lecture and this paragraph unfinished:

> In essence, the conflict that exists today is no more than an old-style struggle for power, once again presented to mankind in semi-religious trappings. The difference is that this time the development of atomic power has imbued the struggle with a ghostly character; for both parties know and admit that, should the quarrel deteriorate into actual war, mankind is doomed. Despite this knowledge, statesmen in responsible positions on both sides continue to employ the well-known technique of seeking to intimidate and demoralize the opponent by marshalling superior military strength. They do so even though such a policy entails the risk of war and doom. Not one statesman in a position of responsibility has dared to pursue the only course that holds out any promise of peace, the course of supra-national security, since for a statesman to follow such a course would be tantamount to political suicide. Political passions, once they have been fanned into flame, exact their victims . . .

The United Nations, formed with high purpose to help resolve problems between and among nations, has, at the very least, presented a vehicle whereby such problems can be discussed and through which attempts at resolutions can be made.

The emergences of science can embroil the world; yet no vehicle exists whereby problems can be discussed between and among scientists without first securing permission from their respective governments, which are essentially interested only in the applications of science.

A supra-scientific entity, perhaps not dissimilar to the United Nations, would offer immense hope to a world in torsion. Such an entity would not involve itself with applications but only with basic science and inquiry in all areas: population - pressures, resources - depletion, water - pollution, air-contamination, accelerating world hunger, increasing torsion among individuals — problems not at all regional in character but basic to the Ecology of Man.

Such an entity could offer clarity to the world instead of charity that bloats the giver and demeans the receiver and could offer at least one beacon in man's continuing search for his own universality.

(October 6, 1961)

IX

The Computerized Intellectuals

MAN NEEDS A new idea of himself for himself; a new perspective to meet a new challenge and a new threat; a new faith, a faith in himself, as a warming assurance against the loneliness of the cosmic cold encroaching upon him with each impressive step of the computerized intellectuals of our time.

To these intellectuals, opinions must either emerge from cleverly designed computer programs or be capable of being verified by such data insertions and manipulations. Man — his continuation, modification, or annihilation — is to them a series of complex formulations readily convertible into electronic impulses. Conclusions drawn from mechanized manipulations with almost lecherous abandon are then considered to be objective, irrefutable, and profound.

The fallacy here is not that man designs and uses amazingly complex equipment, but that his dependence upon his mechanized extensions has become so deep-rooted that he, himself, is increasingly becoming an extension of his own mechanics and is decreasingly capable of functioning as a total human being. This process is being pursued with an acceleration in the name of progress; and an evolutionary coarsening seems to be taking place. Sadly enough, the mechanistic manipulators — prophets of expediency — are highly honored by the society they dishonor.

Mechanistic-man does not here refer to those of his devices that release him from animal-toil — whether in the daily mechanics of living or in the mechanics of the pursuit of knowledge — but rather to those devices that enmesh him in electronic nets and befoul his thinking.

Actually, many tools of daily living, even when they may offer an small measure of seeming comfort, are harmful to the individual and to his community. For example, the automatic garbage-disposal units so common in rabbit-run subdivisions are being outlawed in many areas because they consume too much water and pollute the water consumed by adjacent runs.

Tools used in the pursuit of knowledge frequently hinder the acquisition of knowledge. In medicine, for example, the electrocardiograph is a relatively simple device and easy to operate; but interpretations drawn from electrocardiograms by inexperienced physicians may give doctor and patient either a false sense of well-being or generate baseless fears. Here, the clever tool distinctly hinders the acquisition of knowledge since, without it, knowledge would be pursued and perhaps found along other paths. In this regard, the mechanical tool becomes a crutch to faltering intellects.

The basic approach of the computerized intellectual is essentially defeatist, isolationist, or religionist; and often a combination of the three.

Most of them are defeatist against man himself. Deliberate or accidental nuclear-weaponry-malfunction, they believe, will destroy the world at some calculable point in time. In order to eliminate the risk of total erasure, their solution is for man, now, to eliminate such devices from his arsenal of abilities. However, since man cannot expunge knowledge from the race-memory of the species, the threat of total erasure will always be with us until the inevitable terminal accident. In the opinion of these defeatists, man is therefore doomed — if not in the Biblical sense, then in the computer sense.

Many computerized intellectuals are also isolationist in that they work for governments and the network of government–industry complexes rather than for man. For these complexes, they examine permutations and combinations of imagined possibilities and probabilities which will hopefully terminate in the theoretical vanquishment of the enemy. The enemy is another government and its network of government–industry complexes. In order to retain any sanity many of these scientists attempt to isolate government from people, trying to maintain that their scientific skills and intellectual efforts are directed not at the people of a nation or at the nation itself, but only at the governments of the theoretical enemy nations. Massive weaponry, they maintain, is intended only as a threat to isolate the enemy and will never be used except as a threat. A threat that does not carry direct execution as a highly probable progression has all of the impact of a punch thrown by a shadow-boxer; therefore, they would seem to maintain that bigger weapons are only to throw bigger shadows. Meanwhile, their scientific energies can be devoted to space-penetration. Of course, space-weaponry has an intimate relationship with Earth-weaponry, and anything related to Earth-weaponry automatically opens the coffers of government. Perhaps it is not so strange that when his mechanical extensions take off from launching-pads on their soaring paths man hides in protective bunkers and ventures out only when his instruments assure him of safe exit.

The computerized intellectual is a religionist in that he has total faith in his devices, a ritual for their use which he expresses in jargonistic incantations, and an eternal belief in scientific objectivity isolated from human need. Those who do not believe in this religion are sternly excommunicated and expedited to scientific oblivion; those who do believe may also be doomed — but only accidentally.

The quantitative accumulations of fragments of knowledge, so haphazardly gathered in seeming frenzy, have not brought qualitative changes toward wisdom or toward an appreciation of the individual as the possessor of the indivisible strength of unity. There seem to be irreversible changes in man and his inter-relationship with his environment in which acceleration for its own sake appears to be the least common denominator. It does not seem to matter where we are going so long as we go there speedily. We seem to be forced to move faster in order to keep a little ahead of ourselves. While this is a scientific absurdity, it does make for a nice sort of national goal in all parts of the world. If a project is finished a month or a year ahead of schedule, the nation exults. The possibility that in terms of man's hope and destiny, the project was silly from its inception seems unimportant.

Man, of course, has no destiny without survival. Yet is man's greatest crime the discontinuation of himself? Hardly. There are many reasons for a parent to risk, offer, and give his life for the safety of his child, a safety which neither parent nor child can truly guarantee. We are capable of many acts of bravery under stress where one life is deliberately given for the survival of another, of perhaps lesser merit. Discontinuation of self is not the great crime, nor even discontinuation of the species. Total erasure leaves no destiny and no crime. Man's greatest crime is the threat of total erasure because this threat, directed daily against all people, causes the individual to cease existing as an entity with direct meaning to himself or to anyone else.

In man's constant commitment of his greatest crime we see mass-man reaching the height of importance, while individual-man ceases to have significance — often even to himself. Our computerized intellectuals are capable of extracting their fragments of knowledge only from masses of data; the tools we now possess do not function on an individual basis, but only on a comparative basis. We are in a peculiar age of the mass, physically, culturally, ethically and morally. Mass-man has no problems; he is handed solutions which he follows with as little expenditure as possible of any sort of personal awareness.

The foster father or foster brother image of government is in opposition to the actuality of the individual, since government, of whatever complexion, represents mass-morality within which the individual is stratified and compartmentalized.

If mass-morality is the basic ingredient necessary for the survival of atomic-age-man, he will continue to live with the threat of total erasure. How can the individual who permits mass-morality to envelop him survive and flourish in such a debilitating environment? Obviously he cannot. He is prey to all sorts of virulent attacks, the most potent of which is the thickening haze of moral fallout.

If man is to survive and flourish he must find a new faith in himself as an individual and as a total human being. He must resist being coated by the protective coloration of the mass. Each thought and action each day, assumes infinite importance to the individual in his struggle against deadening absorption.

Man has become part of a strange cycle. There was a time, even in the recent past, when the harm that could be inflicted by pestilence, war, or avarice was confined within regional boundaries, leaving the remainder of Earth free to assist the damaged parts in recovering from their wounds. Somewhere there was a sanctuary for recuperation. Today this is no longer so. Each person is now so intimately placed with another that a blast in one segment of his domicile shakes the entire structure.

Despite our daily disgorging of factual fragments we are living biologically in a parasitic and antagonistic relationship with our Earth, and not at all in a mutually symbiotic relationship. It was not always this way.

Symbiosis generally defines the living together — sometimes in intimate relationship and close union — of two dissimilar organisms, usually for mutual benefit and sometimes because of mutual need. The relationship may be between two plants, two animals, or between an animal and a plant. Occasionally this union results in an organism entirely different from either component.

The lichen, growing in its numerous variations throughout much of the world where human encroachment has not destroyed them, is often cited as an example of true symbiosis. Lichens are composed of a fungus and an alga, living together for mutual benefit. The fungus gains nutriment from the alga, since the alga contains chlorophyll, which is the essential ingredient in photosynthesis, the food-manufacturing process of plants. The alga gains some weather and insect protection from the fungus as well as a needed and increased water supply. When they attach themselves together to rocks and trees as lichen, they help to break down these parent materials into organic and inorganic soils. They are also used as food by various animals, including man.

Another symbiotic relationship is that existing between man and his domesticated food-producing animals. A cow, when properly maintained by man, offers in return for her maintenance a substantial supply of milk which, in one form or another, is an important part of man's food supply. In her final use she offers meat, leather, and hundreds of pharmaceuticals presently extractable from slaughter-house blood and offal.

While she is alive, cow and man have a rather revealing symbiotic relationship. A milk cow, before man forced her into machine-like regularity, could forage for herself. She did not produce nearly as much milk as she presently does; neither was she so dependent upon man for her food supply and maintenance. At one time she was an earth-like chunk of animal vigor, capable of protecting herself and her young. She had food to offer man, but he struggled to secure it. Today, as a result of generations of intensive domestication, the cow can no longer take care of herself and, if left unattended, is subject to all sorts of diseases and internal malfunction. Since her calf is removed from her side shortly after birth, she does not protect her young. Her milk is removed and sold and her calf is raised mainly on various milk-substitutes. But the cow herself produces considerably more milk as a result of her domestication and her symbiotic existence with man.

It is quite foreseeable that the cow will outlive her usefulness to man at some point relatively near in time. When that happens she will not be returned to her previous undomesticated and unsymbiotic habitat, mainly because man will have more intensified need for the Earth-space the cow would use. She will become a curiosity, and the symbiotic relationship between man and cow will cease to exist. This relationship is presently in the process of major basic change in many parts of the world.

The horse, once in symbiotic relationship to man and a source of much of the energy needed by man in his eternal translation of Earth's resources into human use has, within less than fifty years, become a curiosity and a luxury.

It is difficult to think of symbiotic relationships between man and any other organism that are permanently and mutually advantageous.

In terms of agricultural land, man has been able to reclaim deserts for his use by enriching soils and by bringing in the needed water. For a number of years he lives in a productive relationship with this reclaimed land; but then, whenever he intensifies his efforts toward it, the land gradually recedes from productivity. In the reclaimed arid regions of the western United States, thousands of acres return to the desert every year as intensified water-withdrawals cause drops in water-tables and a harmful increase in water-salinity. Intensive withdrawals of liquids from the earth have, in numerous dry regions, caused the land itself to subside. In the Santa Clara Valley of our West, for example, government calculations indicate that the land has sunk more than nine feet within the last fifty years, an astonishingly rapid subsidence for such a brief geologic time.

It would appear that man's relationship with his Earth is essentially parasitic.

Parasitism is an association of organisms in which one lives on or in the body of the other. The parasite lives off the host, consuming the host's ingredients and rendering no service in return. Many parasites are actually dangerous to the host. In medicine, a vast and complex area known as medical-parasitology, is devoted to this subject.

Since the parasite renders no service in return for his nourishment, recuperation, and reproduction needs, the host usually suffers measurable depletion.

What does man return to his host, the Earth?

At one time, when our country was young, its original Americans returned to the land as much as they took from it. This mutualism, a true symbiotic relationship, became part of the ritual of the American Indian. Our land is rich, our resources great, our productivity fabulous, and our generosity in times of stress and catastrophe unquestioned. But toward our land we seem to believe that the bigness of our taking demonstrates the greatness of our comprehension.

In China, family-land used to be maintained for generations in full productivity because its people returned to the fertile land almost as much as they took from it. This mutualism was part of the ritual of the Chinese farmer.

In Holland, England, France, and in many countries of the world such symbiotic relationships existed in varying degrees between man and his Earth. This is no longer true of any nation. Can we return to that time? Nobody can return to anywhere unchanged.

We now deflower the Earth and present her with bouquets of stockpiled weaponry that can, through accident or corruption, obliterate host and parasite.

There was a time in the history of our nation when we carried our frontiers into strange lands sparsely populated with those who knew themselves as Earth-people whose daily lives and ritual were intimately related to the spirit of the land and the heavens. In their symbiotic relationship with the land these early Americans developed cultures toward which we sometimes yearn in the hidden hunger of a national malnutrition. With individual courage, purpose, and pride, our frontiersmen coursed the wilderness in search of space for the expansion of their own potentialities. They merged their cultures, brought from diverse lands and ghettos across the seas, with the culture of the American Indian. But it took a tragically short time for contempt of the prior occupants to permeate the accelerating bustle of the frontier and for bloodshed, avarice, and cheating to muddy this altered environment in the name of expedience and progress. The conscience of the nation was never aroused, except sporadically, against the immorality with which our early frontier was tamed.

Did the first white-man to land in America, by the fact of his existence, inevitably condemn to oblivion the Indian, his culture, and his symbiotic inter-relationship with his Earth?

Today in this country we have what has been called a New Frontier. As we stretch our tentacles toward the frontiers of space, Earth herself has become the jumping-off place — and the race may be to the swift but not necessarily to the wise.

If we were wise, we would explore our relationship to this New Frontier in light of our experiences with the previous one.

Our new frontier is, in reality, far more than space exploration. Eliminating for the moment all rocketry and nuclear devices, all threat of annihilation, all differences among nations, we still have massive problems of man's being replaced by his machines, of increasing populations and increasing hunger, of accelerated diseases and accompanying anguish, of resources-depletion, of water and air pollution — myriad problems, and no quiet time in which to think. A significant point here is that these problems have to do with individual well-being, while rocketry and nuclear devices have to do with government well-being. National aspirations here have little to do with the aspirations of the individual.

With the explosive birth of the atomic age man entered a heterotic existence. Heterosis is the term used to define the hybrid vigor usually found in the initial crossing of different animals or plants. A cross between a Brahma dam and a Hereford bull, for example, will result in a calf in whom the strong features of each parent will usually be combined. The same is generally true of hybrid corn or cross-bred humans.

We, too, are now cross-bred. Our sire is the basic energy never before generated by man, that never before existed as a tool; and our dam is our Mother Earth to which we are bound.

There are many pitfalls in heterosis. While the first cross between two dissimilar breeds is usually stronger than either parent, crossing the offspring with a member of either parent's breed can result in throwbacks that are even weaker than either of the grandparents. For example, the first cross of a Brahma cow and a Hereford bull results in what is sometimes called a Bramford, an animal with marked hybrid vigor. Crossing this Bramford with either a Brahma or a Hereford will result in an unspecified offspring that will usually be less vigorous than the Bramford.

But there is a method of approach that can bring continuing value from heterosis. Should the Bramford be crossed with a Black Angus or a Brown Swiss, for example, the offspring of this mating will usually continue to be strong. Only when these cross-matings have been achieved by design for several generations after a considerable and adequate blending of genes can the latest offspring be crossed back to its ancestors' breed with some assurance of no harmful effects. The Santa Gertrudis is a new and vigorous cattle breed similarly designed in recent years.

This can actually be an object lesson. We have not yet had enough cross-breeding of our basic energy and our earthbound life to allow our scientists, governments, and other segmenters to dominate. In time, after we have learned to live with our heterotic vigor, after we have had an adequate blending of our altered genetic structures, we can return to our scientists and specialists and allow them to serve the whole body of mankind. Until then they should be addressed in a manner reminiscent of the Englishman who signed all his letters to public officials: "You are, Sir, our most humble servant. . ."

It would seem that for our species to survive and flourish each individual must re-kindle faith in himself, in the totality of his own being, in the strength of his own wholeness.

The whole is greater than the sum of its parts because only the whole has the strength of unity. In this sense the individual is the whole, while any government is only the sum of its parts.

Each thought and gesture, each acceptance or rejection of idea, each expression of his code of personal morality, each striving, must reflect to the individual the full strength of his unity. Anything less seems to be a violation of personal dignity.

We have become so much a part of the protective coloration of the mass that each person scarcely recognizes himself and his own value. Obviously we must re-examine our own value to ourselves. While the individual cannot avoid being a statistic within accumulations of data, he can resent and resist being nothing more than a statistic to himself.

If man has any remaining measure of free choice he could well use it to guard against encroachment by those who want to absorb him into the mass, there to become diluted beyond recognition. And he could certainly begin by questioning the wisdom of the computerized intellects of our time. He could insist that the projects of our age, so very costly in terms of the individual, be presented with simplicity and clarity for comprehension by the individual. He could continually maintain that scientific skills be directed away from accelerated man-made threat. He could demand the recognition of himself as a total human being, so to be cherished and respected. And he could be told the extent of his possessions and the true nature of man-made threat, so intimately coupled to man-made promise.

Each person is the center of his universe, and the flow of time is a personal passage to each of us. With benefit to ourselves and to our immediate society, we could frequently ponder where we are, where we have been, and where we are going.

(February 24, 1961)

X

The Emperor's Robe

IN ITS OWN purest essence mathematics can transmit to the world of scientific reality intellectual concepts bordering on a wisdom approaching revelation. This essence is as rare as the scientific wisdom so few in our history have ever possessed.

Except for this rarity, mathematics is the purest form of logic, coordinating and articulating one truth with another. It is method, not substance. Increasingly, however, it is being pressed into magnifying method while degrading substance.

Are we perhaps becoming a mathematized society where everything wants to be related to numbers — a latter-day numerology where the magic combination of the proper sevens and elevens is the goal, itself measurable in numbers?

Today our advanced planners seek solutions for the continued existence of Man on Earth through the manipulation of numbers in what is called the game-theory approach where possibilities and probabilities are translated into mathematical equations. We then attempt to guide the complexity of our lives through the complex medium of our devices, coordinating and articulating the human brain and mind with our intricate computers. Man may not be a series of equations, but we attempt to identify him as such, even if we have to draw him so thin that, unlike the camel, he does pass through the needle's eye.

The new computer wheels of the West to which all of us now pay submission resemble the ancient prayer wheels of the high mountain people of the East. We search heavens for eternity and proscribe ourselves with a high-voltage electronic fence, and we say: Try to go beyond it and you are scorched; touch it, unprotected by the witchcraft of the new Cult of the Technician, and you die.

This hypnosis of numbers — the hypnosis of everything translatable into numbers — is a seeming thing. What then is reality?

When in the wilderness a tree falls and no functioning human ear is available, does it generate sound? If by sound we mean wavelengths capable of being translated by the human ear, the falling tree does generate sound, since if a human ear were present it would translate the wavelengths. To a physicist suddenly deafened, his inability to translate the wavelengths is solely a personal limitation; the falling tree generates a thoroughly comprehensible sound to him, even if thoroughly inaudible. As a matter of fact, if no sound were generated, the physicist's structure of comprehension would be shaken and weakened. The seeming stillness is, in this forest, unrelated to scientific reality.

To a society deafened to reason the stillness is related to ignorance, and to the limitation or absence of substance. The stillness here is also a seeming thing, unrelated to scientific reality. Methods based upon such limitation or absence of substance may be intricately skillful, technically adept, monumentally detailed, even clear-sounding, and be totally unrelated to scientific reality and, therefore, totally invalid.

Such a method, despite massive documentation, is actually scientific vulgarization, and its entire structure is without foundation. It is a glistening mirage of seeming reality which recedes upon the approach of scientific reason. It is the Emperor's Robe, spun of words and numbers, warming through arrogance and ignorance only its wearer since it is a hypnotic weave of no substance and no reality, benefiting only those whose acquisition of personal gain depends upon the Emperor's continued nakedness and the drugged submission of his subjects.

The quiet horror here is that we seem to be increasingly worshipful of such methods, especially when they are intricately documented. Since nearly all this documentation is also extracted from such methods, a parthenogenetic sort of relationship exists where the birthing organism and offspring are genetically identical and are, in a sense, only carbon copies of each other — not only capable of transmitting malfunction from generation to generation, but actually incapable of doing anything else except through mutation.

We seem to be less and less aware of the substance and foundation which can offer stability and variation to the structure of our lives.

The number of choices a person must make to survive and function increases with technical progress, especially when new areas are exposed to human activity. In addition, the constantly varying intensity of choices continually modifies these numbers. Technical progress has also resulted in electronic devices that can manipulate numbers with the speed of light, and with untiring mechanical accuracy and ease far surpassing man's manipulative capacity. Logic then seems dictated that man relinquish many of the numbers of his choices to the machines for them to manipulate with electronic ease and accuracy.

If a concept existed here, it could only be that the machines will hopefully simplify man's choices to himself, not necessarily by reducing their numbers but by assisting him in his quest for clarity by reducing the mechanical toil involved in the manipulation of numbers.

This is precisely what has happened and continues to happen throughout the world of mathematics, particularly in applied mathematics involving devices and verifiable actions. Mathematical possibilities and probabilities are explored with electronic ease and accuracy, and applied mathematical clarity is a continuing achievement in the experimental and verification areas of science.

The basic concepts of the universe created by the theoretical physicists during the monumental scientific revolution of the early Nineteen Hundreds emerged from the nonstandard, unabridged minds of Planck, Einstein, and the others with a clarity and economy of expression that present-day theoreticians could well emulate. These theories, when subsequently verified by experimenters using devices, brought man to a closer concept of the totality of his physical universe. Subsequent devices and actions emerging from theory and needing mathematical clarity and verification are enhanced through refinement of measurement and calculation processes. However, the theoretical standard, subsequently verifiable, remains the basic requirement.

Today we do not possess a theoretical standard for man, and the either–or choice-factor at which our computers are so adept does not apply to man. A measure for man remains elusive. Mathematical values and intricate mathematical models, articulating and coordinating one truth with another in the purest form of logic, are meaningless when applied to a nonexistent standard or measure. This is not essentially because man is infinitely complex, but because logic, regardless of how infinitely pure it is, can neither articulate nor coordinate the currently nonexisting measure of the mathematical value even of individual man, much less that of the inter-relationship of one man with another, and all of man with his total environment.

Attempts to impose mathematical values upon man as a total human being, when a measure for him remains elusive, are clearly unscientific. Such attempts generate chaos instead of assisting in the quest for clarity.

Man's complexity is not the problem; our machines, becoming increasingly more adept, can manipulate complexities. The problem here is straightforward and basic: Our mathematical language at this point is limited because of the absence of the theoretical standard, subsequently verifiable, that could enable us to propose formulations that apply to man. Man's resentment toward the mechanical devices that attempt to direct his actions — regardless of seeming benefit or importance — is from an almost inarticulate awareness that he is not a machine or a grouping of numbers.

Science should certainly seek a theoretical standard for man and then, perhaps, this measure could be expressed mathematically and the weight of electronic devices could then be brought to bear upon man's hope and destiny. Of course, all scientific theoretical search is an attempt to achieve a basic unity. Without basic unity the search must continue, since the theory remains incomplete.

The concept toward Man on Earth must be that man is the universe-in-miniature. The Ecology of Man may develop conceptual standards toward man which may then permit coordination and articulation with infallible logic by his mechanized extensions.

Until science achieves this we are truly the deafened in the wilderness seeing the tree fall but hearing no sound. The stillness is here related to ignorance, not to scientific reality.

Methods based upon this seeming stillness may be intricately
skillful and monumentally detailed with massive documentation, and yet be totally unrelated to scientific reality, and,
therefore, totally invalid.

It may be that science can achieve a basic theoretical
unity toward Man on Earth; it can certainly strive toward
such achievement.

At this point in our primitive probing we are making only
compartmentalized attempts to achieve unity, and this is a
scientific absurdity. We postulate bestiality as a working hypothesis from which we hope to extract clarity and guidance.

The game-theory approach to nuclear war strategy developed by war-scientists throughout the world is especially ad-
mired in our country. In this mathematical game-theory, one
mass of people is given a series of postulations which another
mass of people attempts to anticipate and modify. The participating teams employ possibilities and probabilities which
are calculated mathematically in logical sequences; and attempts at conclusions, accompanied by documentation, are
then made. The aim here is the either–or choice-factor:
capture or stalemate. If the game-theory approach to nuclear
war were merely an exercise of computerized skills and computerized intellects, one could relegate this "Higher Incoher-
ence," as it has been called, to the deflating art form of
Charles Addams. However, this game of the grave is taken
quite seriously by many of today's advanced planners; and
its tally sheets have become part of the paper-strong structure of national and international policy and strategy. Its
scientific absurdities are outbalanced by the physical weight
of its documentation.

Nuclear weaponry cannot be erased from man's arsenal
of abilities and the possibility of total erasure cannot, of
course, be ignored. Science can, and must for its own survival,
bring to bear the full weight of its skills to evaluate the exten-

sions of this possibility and to examine the nature of its probability.

This game-theory of warfare stems from John von Neumann's and Oskar Morgenstern's *Theory of Games and Economic Behavior* (Princeton, N.J.: Princeton Univ. Press, 1944). Two years after its publication it was hailed as a landmark in the history of ideas. "Ten more such books and the progress of economics is assured," was one of its accolades. During the past fifteen years, however, game-theory has contributed little to the solution of economic problems, but much to military tactics and expenditures.

Economic analysts in New York, Chicago, and London, representing billions of dollars of capital investments, keep on spending millions of dollars on game-theory projects in attempts to achieve large capital gains in the concentrated market places of the world. While these attempts refine the logical processes and present electronic ease for the assimilation of data, they cannot replace judgment; neither can they present formulas for the achievement of gambling gains at race courses or financial bourses.

The underlying insight in game-theory is that "parlor-games, economic markets, and military battles are all instances of social situations in which the participants pursue conflicting interests. Moreover, the fate of each participant — the poker-player's winnings, the firm's profits, the army's casualties depend, in part, on the actions of other participants. Let us call such a situation, in which the outcome is controlled jointly by a number of participants with incompatible objectives, a game. . ."

In game-theory the question is: "How should a rational person involved in a game act?" And a game, by definition, shall mean "a social situation in which there are several individuals, each pursuing his own interest, and in which no single individual can determine the outcome. Parlor games, of course, fulfill this definition . . . so does much of warfare. . . ."

This definition of "game" in game-theory approach cannot apply to nuclear warfare, since a single individual or participating unit can at least theoretically determine the outcome of nuclear war. If a single individual or unit possessed a sufficient stockpile of devices and their means of delivery, and if, for any reason, these devices were suddenly hurled against a hemisphere, the outcome is determined.

Furthermore, game-theory presupposes both a winner and a loser. In nuclear warfare it is at least theoretically possible that neither participant wins but that both lose.

Game-theory of warfare eliminates even the theoretical possibility of both participants losing. This is not stalemate, where neither side wins and, therefore, by implication, neither side loses. Where both sides lose, where is the win factor? Game-theory here states that equal fear, equally shared, is progress. This is clearly ridiculous.

Game-theory cannot apply where one theoretical possibility must be ignored as though it did not exist.

An ancient Persian proverb has clearer application here: "If the first building-stone is askew, the structure may reach to the heavens, and all of it be crooked."

The either–or choice-factor in the game-theory of nuclear warfare is clearly represented in the logical thinking of a well-publicized American physicist who is dedicated to the concept that when a "limited nuclear war" is in progress we shall be much better prepared than in times of peace; therefore, during a limited nuclear conflict would be the worst time for the enemy to launch an "all-out attack." The way to assure peace, according to this logic, is to get into a war immediately, and stay there forever. Thereby, peace will be assured. Of course, the war this physicist seems to advise is a limited nuclear war — probably for limited people.

Unhappily, there is no end to such idiocies emerging from insolent and unprincipled scientists.

The various mathematical calculations within the either–or choice-factors of destruction are usually rigid and unilateral. They omit from their "postures" either–or factors relating to the possible combination of chemical, bacteriological, and nuclear warfare because they quite actually "posture" a sort of international rule book, with an umpire who will cry "foul!" if one of the participants in this game-theory performs in a manner not previously considered.

All of them omit the inter-relationship between massive death and the resultant torsion in the living, with attendant debilitations: Epidemic and pandemic disease that follow massive destruction; the survivor's abilities to recuperate; the bio-ecologic cycle affecting plants and animals; water-pollution through radiation; chemical and decay-contamination; subsoil percolation and the possibilities of ground-water contamination that can endure for centuries; total watershed contaminations that can reach across a continent; grave climatic modifications resulting from massive disturbances of the bio-ecologic cycle; ocean contaminations through deliberate or inaccurate bombings; wind-tunneling effects about which we know very little. So very many things are left out of their computerized calculations, especially those regarding recuperation capabilities. Whatever conclusions they extract through their mysterious and alchemistic manipulations have no bases in scientific reality and are, quite actually, gibberish.

It is true that we know little about many factors, but our lack of knowledge about them cannot be accepted as license to ignore them as though they did not exist.

The projected solutions of these either–or gamblers who are playing with their devices are based on massive burial. Entomb the dead and incarcerate the living.

The post-atomic-age scientist, playing with his devices, seems to be a genetic mutation resulting from the massive

moral fallout apparently more cumulative in the tens of
thousands of scientists and technicians who exist, profession-
ally and personally, actually and only because of the threat
of total erasure. The elimination of this threat would eliminate most of them, and they struggle for survival as does any
organism. As an organism, this type of ugly and not so quiet
scientist is assured nourishment by others whose major gains
also result only from a continuing threat of total erasure.
His recuperation is assured him by the acquisition, with ease,
of whatever environment and protection from sanity he thinks
he needs; this environment is assured him by those who also
assure him nourishment. His reproduction is parthenogenetic,
so that he continually births others identical to himself.
Those who, for personal gain, assure him nourishment and
recuperation also assure him that the quantity of offspring
is the only true measure of the quality of his fertility.

Can we accept this mutant as a man, as a total human
being? More important, must we? We can well ponder the
nature of its morality and ethics, and its total lack of objectivity.

Its publications, mainly, are operations manuals for the
continued survival, not of mankind, but of this particular
organism, of this mutant.

The continuing parthenogenetic birthing has created a
huge number of these parasitic organisms, who seek ways and
means to force the host body of mankind to contribute ever-
more of the basic requirements they need for their continued
existence.

To the continued existence of their cult they bring to bear
all refined skills of their trade. Jargon is their fence to keep
out reality; and they charge this fence with measured surges
of fear.

Since operations manuals for this fence or stockade are
needed by the cult, we shall probably be weighted by many
of them. The scientific credence of these manuals has all of

the logic of a plea that the child who murders his father and his mother must be shown clemency, because he is now an orphan.

Death is, of course, a fact measurable in numbers; the number of man-made five million or 500 million dead is certainly measurable; but the meaning is not at present measurable. The quantitative reduction from the pool of mankind may be measurable, but not the qualitative modification.

The surgeon on his way to the hospital to operate on the only witness to the innocence of a prisoner on trial is killed in a highway accident. The surgeon dies; the witness dies; the prisoner is found guilty; and the justice of a nation is polluted by the jailing of an innocent man. Is this measurable in numbers?

Suppose then, that the surgeon was killed in some manner after the operation was successful, and justice did emerge for the innocent. Is the surgeon's death then measurable in numbers? Is justice here measurable in the accidental relationship of the time of its occurence? Does today's war-science dictate that justice is a random factor of measurable accident?

Death is a fact of numerous interrelationships, many of which are measurable and many of which are not. One hundred dead are more than ten times greater than ten dead. There is a seeming geometric factor here in terms of interrelationships for which we do not, as yet, have a theoretical standard.

Even as a terminal factor death, and its inter-relationships with the living and their total environment, does not lend itself to a calculable formulation. Glib inanities involving 50 million or 100 million dead people are a corruption of mathematics and a relegation of what is called science to the playpen of the inept.

While the essence of mathematics can transmit to scientific reality intellectual concepts bordering on a wisdom approaching revelation, our theoreticians of the grave are striving to pollute this essence with piercing disharmonies from their pious orgies of self-righteousness.

It would seem imperative that science address itself toward the achievement of a basic theoretical unity toward Man on Earth. This was always the quest of science — for its own survival and for human striving.

(March 24, 1961)

XI

The Tentacles of Science

THE SEARCH FOR the clarity needed to dispel confusion and uncertainty is an individual search and an individual responsibility. In many ways our environment of accelerated confusion and uncertainty is directly attributable to an idolatry of things scientific; and perhaps even more to our haste in abdicating on a personal basis our honor, dignity, and sense of value.

Our trust in many aspects of science may be displaced to our individual detriment; so many of its tentacles, mislabelled science, are not science at all.

Science is accumulated knowledge, systematized and formulated with reference to the discovery of general truths and the operation of general laws. These general laws, subsequently verifiable, are arrived at mainly through induction and hypothesis. Induction is a process of reasoning from a part to a whole, from particulars to generals, from the individual to the universal. Hypothesis is a tentative theory or supposition, provisionally adopted to explain certain facts and to guide in the investigation of others. Using induction and hypothesis, science attempts to arrive at general truths and general laws in whatever area it functions.

Attempts at a unified theory of science strive toward universal truths and universal laws which are subsequently verifiable.

Most scientific aspects of our complex society, and their technologic applications to almost every segment of our lives, are related to science as a child is related to its parent. The parent is mother or father to the child, but the child is neither mother nor father to the parent. And not all children are assets; some become enemies of society.

Throughout history, science, unfettered by the shackles of expediency, has been one of man's noblest pursuits; and we are all profoundly indebted to those few who have devoted, and are devoting, their lives to it in their quest for knowledge and human enrichment.

Today, however, many of the offspring of science have become enemies of society mainly because we have permitted our individual conscience and awareness to become dulled by the hypnotic repetition of false promises made by those who speak in the name of science.

Today, if a pertinent question begins to emerge from human conscience and awareness, it is inundated by a mass of answers. Even if we do not know to which questions they apply, we still have answers. Many who speak in the name of science self-righteously cite the 60 million or so pages of technical writing now published annually on our planet, in addition to the estimated 60 thousand scientific and technical books, the 100 thousand research papers, and the more than one million scientific and technical articles produced yearly, as an indication of the huge numbers of answers we are acquiring with almost automated efficiency. There are not this many new things emerging annually from the world's scientific and technical minds. This paper blizzard both chills our search for knowledge and tends to make us huddle in deep recesses of our own minds in an effort to escape from a reality we hesitate to explore.

The plethora of answers to a paucity of questions gives us a false sense of knowledge and hinders the attempt of each of us to retain freedom as an individual — as a total human being. We are enmeshed in a net — not of science, but of its numerous offspring seeking particular bits and pieces for immediate personal gain while increasingly disregarding the implications of their endeavors to man.

Compared to man, any species is a model of economy and utility. Today we devote fantastic sums and energies to the accumulation of stockpiles of scientific garbage. A small percentage of the stockpile can be used as mulch and fertilizer for human enrichment; the remainder pollutes our thinking and presents disposal problems.

One of the main sources of this garbage throughout the world is, unfortunately, universities. So very much of what is called research at many universities is no more than applied science and gadgetry, contracted, paid for, and supervised by governments and industries. Such contracts are seducing universities into becoming appendages to government–industry complexes. Of course contract-research has its value; but it smothers scholarship. For their survival it would seem that universities should reject such research and return to being seats of learning. Most universities would suffer financial losses because of such rejections, which might be a good thing. Universities should not become outposts for government-industrial complexes or emporia of study where basement bargains are available, and where annual clearance sales are held with pomp and ceremony. The resignation of personnel who find contract-research more rewarding than scholarship would help de-pollute our atmosphere and would strengthen universities in their historic role in the way discriminate pruning strengthens a sturdy tree.

Unhappily, so much of science has become incomprehensible to scientists and utter gibberish to nonscientists.

Language is a medium for the exchange of ideas. Jargon, the technical vocabulary of science, is a vehicle for the transmission of facts. As jargon becomes more and more the medium of technical expression all over the world, the gap widens between ideas and facts. Each becomes increasingly distrustful of the other. In a society that cherishes fragments of data and is disdainful of anything it cannot label or compartmentalize, perhaps this is unavoidable. But it is regrettable.

The cherishing of facts and disdaining of ideas so enmeshes us in the mechanics of living that we lose comprehension of ourselves and our society. It is as though our excellent vehicles have annihilated our sense of, and need for direction. We do not care where we have been, do not know where we are, and cannot tell where we are going.

Our facts are voluminous; our purpose skimpy.

We cannot assume that scientific progress, as such, brings wider understanding. Quite to the contrary. While language barriers among nations are gradually crumbling, new barriers are being generated within nations by data-gatherers, devotees of jargon.

In our fact-laden society the jargon spin-off of a biochemist working, let us say, in genetics, may be understandable to a French-speaking biochemist working in genetics; but it is nearly incomprehensible to his English-speaking physicist team-colleague; and neither biochemist nor physicists understands the team radiologist.

Of course, every science and discipline needs a terminology which it finds absolutely essential for self-expression; but too often this terminology becomes a fence behind which the ignorant or pretentious hide. Frequently the cadences which reach our ears are nothing more than a ritual for autohypnosis in words that are not even jargon but gibberish.

We cannot have too much science; but we certainly can have too much gadgetry, application, and gibberish that limit or grossly disregard the search for truth and law and human striving.

We accept too many things that need to be questioned before they become too intimately woven into the fabric of our lives, there to become a shroud, suitable only for the burial ceremony.

If our existence has become a high-speed race, where are we headed? Toward what goal? We can certainly pause long enough to try to secure bearings on the direction toward which we are either pushing ourselves or being pushed. If we are escaping, then from what are we escaping? And into what?

Applied scientists are devoting their energies to bringing about a wedding of man and his machines. As tools become more and more involved and more and more capable of taking over so many of the functions of man, the nuptial night approaches. One wonders at the contemplated offspring of such a marriage.

Of course, machines and devices are permanent adjuncts to our society throughout the world. It is not a question of whether or not we should build the machines; we could scarcely avoid building them. But we must exert our skills to seek concepts regarding the inter-relationship of our devices with our society. We must question the implications of the machines to our lives — not necessarily because machines replace people, but because increased dependence upon ma-

chines mechanizes the individual to that point of brittleness
which is so easily shattered.

Dependence upon devices, accompanied by reduced appreciation of the individual, can destroy liberty.

Automation can here be used as an example. Automation
is certainly inescapable. Its tentacles reach out to touch
or squeeze almost every aspect of human endeavor — from the
teaching of the young through automated instruction — as is
being done in some schools — to much of the medical care of
the terminally ill in some modern hospitals where automated
devices check patients' temperatures, blood-pressures and
pulse-rates, and deliver and remove food trays at proper
intervals. When the gauges cease to record, the gauge-watcher
knows that the patient is dead. It is quite conceivable to
design and build completely automated schools and hospital
wards — both utterly antiseptic.

There are many advantages in automation, and the quantity of finished product that can be delivered day after day
after day is fabulous. The cost of automation, however, is
like an iceberg whose greater part is hidden from view.
Standardization of product encourages standardization of
use, which encourages standardization of people and distrust
of the individual who is neither standardized nor catalogued.
In our society we have numerous examples of such distrust.
If such standardization is protective coloration of the mass,
against what is this protection offered? Who is the enemy?
In this context individualism is obviously the enemy. Must
we then conclude that a technically complex society cannot
tolerate individuals?

Automation would not be possible without computers,
mathematical recording, cataloguing, and manipulating devices whose influences are everywhere felt — from the first
spaceship to orbit our planet all the way to the number and

variety of toilet tissues a supermarket chain should order for its various outlets.

In our complex society computers are essential in the performance of a variety of jobs with electronic ease and accuracy. However, we seem to have accepted them and their refinements with a near-total disregard to their implications.

Computers are electronic depositories of miscellaneous bits and pieces of correct or incorrect information, all readily extractable.

Almost everyone today is in somebody's notebook, somewhere. From the moment of birth he becomes a note, written and extractable. Later, there are school records, medical history records, all sorts of licensing information, voting registration information, employment data, magazine preferences from mailing lists, book preferences from library check-out cards, tax-payment information, social security notes, financial transactions through bank checks, consumer-research poll responses, references, dossiers — all sorts of information and miscellaneous minutiae are written and extractable.

Computers are extraordinarily adept at storing and sorting this type of information. Certainly it is logical to expect that at some point a gigantic computer-system will be built in some underground installation, where all the miscellaneous information on every person in the country will be stored, sorted, and extractable. As soon as the individual does anything recordable, it could automatically be transmitted to the nation's master-computer, there to become part of the individual's manipulative record.

This concentration of information is also a vast concentration of power of the gravest implications to personal dignity and liberty. Under whose thumb will this power rest? Can such power be entrusted to any one person, or to any group, of whatever persuasion?

Yet such a master-computer, which can really record the fall of the sparrow, and which can truly become the Ancient

Book in which all is writ, is an almost inevitable fact. Too many seeming advantages could accrue from Master-Computer-U.S.A., and Master-Computer-U.S.S.R., or from Master-Computer-West and Master-Computer-East for it to be disregarded. Our own national mechanical skills, coupled to our national disregard for personal privacy and our national acceptance of standardization, offer peculiarly fertile ground for the erection of our master-computer, perhaps in the not-too-distant future.

From numerous approaches a thoroughly logical plea can be made for such a master-computer. It could actually help find jobs for those unemployed through automation or through other causes. It could make good the personnel boast of fitting the man to the job and the job to the man. The unemployed would have to be catalogued in terms of present skills, schooling, references, and preferences; and the jobs, too, would have to be catalogued in terms of needed skills, schooling, references, and preferences. In order to keep the master-computer functioning properly, no job-holder could change his job, or job-seeker accept one, without first securing approval from the master-computer. Also, no new jobs could be created or old ones eliminated without the master-computer's recognition and approval.

All of these are really elementary manipulations for even an unsophisticated computer. There is no question but that given these restrictions the master-computer could help reduce unemployment and guarantee promotion to the deserving in a thoroughly proper and orderly manner. It could, quite readily, determine our national consumptive capacity in terms of the products our automated factories should turn out; and wasteful stockpiles of unsold products could become a thing of the past.

While this sort of control is presently repulsive to us, the ingredients for such control already exist.

Everyone, of course, is interested in health. The master-computer could be invaluable in improving certain aspects of our national health. Several instrumentation laboratories are attempting to develop what is called a personal biochemical profile, to be taken at birth and then checked annually. Biologically, people age at different rates and, for the same person, various organs also age biologically at different rates. Relatively simple biochemical analyses should be able to determine the rate of aging of people and their various organs. It is believed that this information could be used to extend the life-span quite considerably, and to offer important contributions to medicine.

The securing of such biochemical analyses is not very complicated; however, their meaning has not yet been determined. This can be accomplished essentially from statistical extractions. If ten different biochemical analyses are made on samples drawn from a million subjects, and if these subjects are periodically checked, meaning can then be extracted for these anlyses and a long forward stride taken in public health. Obviously, a master-computer would be an ideal device for such statistical extractions, provided that all the individuals involved were thoroughly detailed for ingestion and recording by the master-computer. Once this information is electronically available, the next logical step is to use it for other purposes by other people.

Our technical and scientific progress carries along with it some rather terrifying implications for the individual and his freedom, of which we seem to have only a slight awareness.

Are we, then, really hooked to this unbreakable line of progress, waiting only to be netted?

Hopefully, not really and not yet.

Attempts have recently been made to formulate courses of graduate study under the general title of Medical Ecology,

for the purpose of evaluating the inter-relationship of one ailment with another, and with the sum of the ailments and pre-
scribed courses of treatment and their responses as they affect
the individual patient.

Attempts are also being made to use electronic computers
in medical diagnosis. Various specialists feed into a computer
data listing various symptoms and their combinations. Tentative diagnoses resulting from a combination of the programmed symptoms are also inserted into the machine. When the
proper patient-data are later fed into the machine, the correct
diagnosis should hopefully emerge.

This is a brittle sort of specialization that has only mod-
erate value, because Medical Ecology is still in its infancy
and medical inter-relationships remain mainly unknown.

For example: The term "availability" in ecology refers
not to the presence of a particular ingredient, but to the
presence and availability for use of that ingredient by a
particular organism. The presence of the ingredient can be
detected through various laboratory techniques, but whether
or not it is available for use depends upon numerous and
variable factors. In soil science the acidity–alkalinity relationship known as pH directly affects the release or lockup
from the soil of certain present ingredients and makes them
available or unavailable to the particular plant at a particular
time. Altering the pH so that the soil acidity–alkalinity balance is changed can lock up a particular ingredient so that it
is not available for use to the plant regardless of what quantities of the ingredient are present.

We know a great deal about pH lockup principles in soils,
but little about it in medicine. Yet the lockup principle
applies to each of us in our daily lives, and affects our physical
and nonphysical well-being.

We grasp this principle whenever we begin to recognize
the nature of cause-and-effect. When we alter the equivalent
of the acidity–alkalinity relationship in our own minds, what

ingredients toward understanding, heretofore present but locked up, become available? Is this also true of governments and of individuals who profess to represent man, his present and his future? Of course it is.

We must attempt to evolve some sort of conceptual philosophy toward our scientific progress. Certainly we live under the pressure of immediacy, in the hope that distant tomorrow will be at least as good as today. Our planning skills for tomorrow seem to be directed toward devices and products rather than toward ideas, concepts, and implications.

How can we benefit from our devices without losing our liberty and individuality? This question must become, quite actually, the primary concern of our scientists and philosophers. And if the caves of specialization deepen, perhaps the data-accumulations resulting from this deepening can be sifted astutely with the aid of an emerging science, so that the precious metals of meaning can be extracted and used for the future of man.

The Ecology of Man is the science of his inter-relationship with his total environment.

To his environment, man, in 1945, added the threat of total annihilation. This modification of man's environment was sudden. In a direct sense it was a mutation, presently irreversible, of immediate and permanent impact. Living with this threat modifies both man and his environment.

Perhaps the primary modification is the elimination of discrimination. Nuclear devices do not recognize racial distinctions in their ultimate purpose and effects. All people are affected almost similarly by radiation. Nuclear devices also do not recognize geographic distinctions. Even economic distinctions in terms of nuclear weaponry are gradually disappearing as new techniques make it increasingly easy for many countries to build, possess, and explode such devices.

Thus far, the elimination of discrimination is only in terms of annihilation. However, we must develop methods of approach to enable us to live with this environmental modification. We cannot depend upon our clever devices to evolve useful methods of approach.

Do we possess instrumentation by which man can understand himself — his past, present, and probable future? Such instrumentation cannot exist in exotic pieces of sophisticated hardware which, by design and function, widen the gap between language and jargon, ideas and facts.

The question has never been whether or not machines can think, but whether or not man, enmeshed by machines, can think of and comprehend his own society. Instrumentation for comprehension can perhaps be developed, but only after we have evolved a design-theory for Man on Earth.

At this point in time we should certainly ponder who or what put the ring in our nose and is pulling on the chain, who or what is the prod-stick juicing us by jerks along which path, headed where?

(December 16, 1960)

XII

The Acquiescent Society

MANKIND, AS AN Earth-resource, achieves renewability only through the individual who may, himself, not be renewable. No one recaptures the day of his birth or even this day; nor will tomorrow be recapturable once it is past. You may not have known your grandfather's grandfather and may never know your grandchild's grandchild. You are here because the former existed; and because you are here the latter could come into existence. While nothing you can do will alter the prior fact of your ancestor, any number of probable happenings can destroy the possibility of the subsequent existence of your progeny. There is a full spectrum of new man-made risks to which we have become heir.

Truly we live in an age of perplexity, of distractive uncertainty and bewilderment, not only toward our future but toward the comprehension of our present; and the scream of the lost in the night is unheard and unanswered.

Man's search for knowledge is as basic as the biologic beat of his heart; neither can cease and life continue. For this assertion each of us can present documentation from personal experience and reference. Search cannot be separated from living even when knowledge acquired through search is used for destruction. The search is inevitable. Use of the acquisition, however, is sometimes evil.

The foundation of all religions and philosophies, in their repeated attempts to find man's place in nature, has been this historic dilemma of good-versus-evil. This historic dilemma now seems to be obsolete because a new dimension has been added to the relationship of the search for and the acquisition of knowledge; a dimension which orphans us from our past and menaces our future. The new dimension, a result of scientific search, is the theoretical possibility of man's total erasure. Not total erasure itself but its threat is the ultimate evil. The inevitable search has now resulted in an acquisition that can, theoretically, obliterate the search itself. This is an ultimate dilemma; and this is where man now stands in his relationship with all of nature. It is the unhappy result of man's gradual acquiescence and descent into the mass.

Total erasure used to be God's prerogative. Now it is man's.

If search cannot be separated from living, then the search for methods of approach leading to the solutions of this ultimate dilemma is the basic need for Man on Earth whose place in nature itself must be reexamined. It would seem that man is now more than ever intimately inter-related with all the resources of nature and that his survival can come only from his renewability. Unless we contribute something of ourselves, of our possessions of strength, courage, and wisdom, we may scarcely be a renewable resource. If we are not, we may now

well be witness to the declining days of the final golden age
of man, as he constantly exhausts his planet of its physical
and human resources beyond the point of renewability.

Man's relationship with his life-supporting land is receding and its bounty is increasingly unrecognizable as coming
from the Earth. The technical progress of society makes it
increasingly difficult for the young to recognize the original
source of their sustenance — which so many now seem to
believe is the gaudy package in glittering display.

Our promise of Earth's abundance — which we grasp to
ourselves as a warming assurance of our own continuation —
is dependent upon our vigorous skill in the comprehension
and use of our resources. Translating these resources into
human use requires far more than man's mechanical ingenuity; it requires, essentially, his refined ability to plan for
the future and his discriminating restraint in the use of his
present possessions.

A possession is that to which the possessor has contributed
something of himself; it is neither purchasable nor replaceable in the same degree. An acquisition is that which is
readily purchasable and replaceable.

The noble resources of our Earth have more often been
considered acquisitions than possessions by its peoples.

The mounting torsion throughout the world, the individual stresses and strains — even among the peoples of those
nations now entering the vortex of our technologic society —
probably results from man's isolation from and incomprehension of himself as one of the resources of all of nature. Man
is now aware, even though only in the dim recesses of uncomfortable consciousness, that he, too, can quite literally
become as extinct as many of Earth's prior resources. And
he does not know where to find solace. Is his Earth no longer
stable because he no longer walks erect upon it but seeks

safety in its depths and flexes his manhood in underground weaponry-silos?

We are the total of our resources; when they are depleted we, also, are depleted; when we acquiesce in their depletion we acquiesce in our own.

The three million square miles of our vast North America gave its early settlers a delusion of plenty and richness; and when, through ignorance and mismanagement, the earth was pillaged and became barren there was seemingly endless new land for the taking. In the late Eighteen Hundreds bison by the hundreds of thousands roamed the Great Plains in well-ordered migration patterns — as they had done for centuries. By the Nineteen Thirties, fifty years or so after plows had broken the sod, dust storms from these Plains irritated the conscience of a nation; and disordered migrations of mis-placed families further weakened a dispirited economy. The acquisitive and acquiescent attitudes of man toward his re-sources were certainly major causes for the removal of this land from his reservoir of wealth.

Who can measure the value of one productive acre of Earth? To a farmer in the Orient it may mean the actual difference between life and death for his family. To a dairy farmer in Midwestern U.S.A. it may be worth the price of a good cow. To a beef rancher in our Far West it may be worth the price of a fair calf. To a subdivider it may be worth half the price he asks for one of his houses. To a city dweller it may have no relevance to his needs as far as he is concerned. To the employee of a vast agricultural complex in the U.S.A. or U.S.S.R., driving a huge crawler-tractor pulling discs and harrows in the preparation of the land for planting, an acre is just about enough room in which to make one turnaround.

How can anyone measure the awe and the renewability of a fertile acre of land to a growing child or a fatigued adult?

The food-yielding earth can be a renewable resource; and the good acre — as China has proven in the past — can remain productive for thousands of years if properly maintained. But when this life-resource is placed under unnatural pressure for increased yields, it rapidly recedes from renewability — a recession with which we are all probably somewhat familiar throughout the many layers of our own lives whenever we, ourselves, are unnaturally pressed for increased yields.

In the worldwide drive for increased crop-returns, doses of additives are applied in increasing amount and varieties to the point where the land, her crops, and her people become addicted to their own peculiar man-induced drug-patterns. For a time, returns increase in proportion to the addiction. The cycle then demands increased dosages or attempts at withdrawal. Accelerated dosing carries along with it its own peculiar problems and hallucinations, while attempts at withdrawal bring on symptoms not dissimilar to drug-withdrawal agonies in humans — for the land, too, is alive.

Somehow, the attitude has grown like thistles that the bigger the land-holding the more efficient the operation. This feeling seems to be prevalent both toward individual or corporate farmland ownerships in this country and toward the commune farmland ownership in the U.S.S.R. and China. When thousands of acres are planted to a single crop, the utilization of equipment and manpower may be startlingly efficient; but the utilization of the land as a producing organism and as a renewable resource may be quite inefficient, and the relationship of the manhour worker to the land extremely impersonal and inefficient. There is a point beyond which bigness, of itself, becomes grotesque and mechanical and human efficiency become diluted by the inability of the land to respond to the unnatural demands placed upon it.

Bigger tractors to haul around bigger cultivators and combines; deeper augur-plows to break up soils two, three, and more feet beneath the surface; heavier pumps tap falling water-tables; cleverer chemical compounds to replace lost soil ingredients and to combat mounting disease and insect depredations — all are a testament to man's mechanistic ingenuity, but are no indication of his planning ability or discriminating restraint toward the renewability of his resources and himself.

In our country we are gradually becoming transformed into a synthetic agriculture, where the land is being used increasingly as little more than a retainer for chemicals that are externally applied — a sort of hydroponic system where plants are grown in chemicals dissolved in the water carrier. There is nothing wrong with crops grown hydroponically; as a research tool hydroponic agriculture is extremely valuable. If only our marginal lands were being so used, this technique could be quite beneficial. However, in our unplanned drive to increase yields, even our best lands are being used more and more in a hydroponic manner, adding to our growing stockpiles of agricultural surpluses.

When measured against simultaneously increasing world hunger, our food-stockpile is witness to the crude depletion of our resources and against ourselves, and makes of us a world symbol of material crassness. The reasons behind the stockpile accumulation and our ineptitude in alleviating world hunger are complex. They were planted during our industrial and mechanical revolutions and are now germinating in our scientific revolution in agriculture. Regardless of reason and complexity, however, the existence of so vast a food hoard in a hungry world is a brutalizing factor affecting, in some measure, everyone in the hoarding country. This is part of the cost we are paying for progress. It would seem that progress itself should be examined.

Bio-ecologists are increasingly worried that data concerning the inter-relationship of plants, animals, and man-made and man-altered environments will not be available in an integrated form soon enough to insure broad conservation of our natural resources.

Conservation, of course, means the intelligent use of our resources for the longest possible period of time. It does not mean leaving the forest untouched merely to offer city dwellers an opportunity for a walk in the woods; nor does it mean locating the proper geologic formations for the building of dams merely to create recreation lakes and adjacent picnic areas to lease out to private concessions. The forest has many essential uses beyond conservation; and every dam constructed by man will eventually fill with silt and dry out. Conservation should be more concerned, let us say, with the inter-relationship of a natural resource recreation facility within reach of a large city and the daily accelerating workload of that city's mental health clinics.

The worldwide expansion of acquiescence and its accompanying irresponsibility, as each segment hastens to achieve mechanized ease and plenty, has generated worldwide concern among bio-ecologists who cannot accept synthetic boundaries established by geographic segmenters. Insects and other organisms do not draw the same physical lines of demarcation that man does. Wind-drifts carry pollens and spores over the Earth without regard to individual land ownership or cultural practices. In a few hours jet aircraft can bring organisms from areas of departure to areas of arrival; and feeder aircraft radiating from international fields can spread these organisms with such amazing rapidity that those indigenous to one part of the world can find new habitats thousands of miles away in less than a day. To the bio-ecologist, our excellent vehicles are certainly helping to weld our geographic fragments and unify our concern for Earth's resources.

Most governments of the world are pursuing policies to remove the farmer from small holdings and combine these acres into large units to be worked with advanced equipment. While many small farms are truly inefficient in terms of production, the huge farm-complexes are equally inefficient in terms of sustained yields and preservation and renewability of resources; and they are nakedly inefficient in terms of man's understanding of his inter-relationship with his Earth. In this regard, it should be noted that the rich valleys of our country that produce amazing volumes of crops have been in production for less than a hundred years. Nobody really knows how long they can remain at their present stage of artificially stimulated fecundity — not only because of land exhaustion and chemical contaminations about which we know very little, but essentially because of an environmental pollution generated by such agriculture about which we know even less.

New techniques and lightweight devices, new knowledge and cultural practices can make workable farm units out of 40- or 80-acre holdings that can more than compete, pound-for-pound of harvested yield, with the gigantic agri-business or agri-commune complexes. Such techniques and devices are being used with stimulating success in England, Holland, and parts of Scandinavia. A community of farms in the ecologic sense — with a community of homes and industries — would strengthen not only the land but the national economies and purposes as well. Each part of the community would contribute to the other something of itself; and a symbiotic relationship of lasting value could be established.

The plow-stick of the Orient is certainly not the most efficient agricultural tool devised by man. Neither is the agri-business complex of the U.S.A. or the agri-commune complex of the U.S.S.R. the most efficient tool in man's eternal translation of his resources for human use. Our new knowledge and techniques can well be used to return people to the land rather than to remove them.

This is not just a nostalgia for the homestead and the picket fence. As our feeling for the land becomes increasingly remote we recede from the roots of our strength. There are many inescapable reasons why intimacy with the land is essential for its proper long-range utilization and preservation; and there are many more values to be gained from the earth than the mere number of bushels it can produce per acre. The land offers a broad and rooted foundation upon which to build the structure of the community. Yet governments are now committed to a policy of removing people from family farms which are considered as uneconomic units in terms of gross mechanized production. These people are being jostled into the cities, there to seek what solace they can in job re-training and job hunting.

Midwestern America, in particular, is now peppered with small-farm communities strangled by such policies. The younger people have left for the cities; the older people, mostly women, remain; and a child walking along the town's broad dead streets is a rare sight. Most of the houses are empty and the women have joined each other in the decaying homes of dying communities. The land remains rich but the holdings are too small for economic manipulation by mechanized planners and devices.

To question the bigness of equipment rather than the smallness of philosophy toward the land is to voice a heresy that threatens the present concept of agriculture.

At one time 40 acres constituted a farm of fair size from which a diversified crop could be raised. Today, in many parts of the world, a farm of 400 acres is considered too small a unit for the proper utilization of our mechanized equipment and people, even for a single commercial crop.

To the city dweller and his society this aspect of hugeness often defies imagination. Everything about our agriculture is rendered outsize by the vastness of our land. For example: We produce in the U.S.A. some 200,000 tons of raisins a year, and almost all of it in California's San Joaquin Valley. Black raisins are made by sun-drying grapes. The procedure is to place paper trays on the ground between the rows of vines. Bunches of grapes, as clipped from the vines, are then placed on these trays to dry in the sun. The number of paper trays used every year in this process is around 100 million. Placed end-to-end they would stretch for 40,000 miles. And all this is only for the drying of grapes in the field. In the Los Angeles area the amount of alfalfa brought in to feed dairy cows reaches some 700,000 tons a year. It takes some 25,000 truckloads of double-trailer highway rigs traveling a total of some five million miles for this haul. Consider the fuel, tires, men, equipment, and machine-made pollution involved in transporting such a quantity of hay into one area. In western U.S.A. the number of lug boxes used to haul tomatoes, peaches, and other similar crops from producing fields to processing plants or into storage is something like 40 million. Almost everything within the agricultural complex is numerically huge. We delude ourselves if we attempt to equate numerical bigness with national greatness.

Quite often the California farmer does not own the land he farms. He is a farmer by virtue of owning a portable arsenal of farm equipment; and he obtains crop leases from land owners who are not farmers. The land he farms may be owned by banks, canneries, processing companies, food brokers, estate-holdings — all absentee owners. This farming tendency is steadily increasing in the Far West and is making substantial inroads in other parts of our country.

In Holland, polder-lands are reclaimed from the sea by building dikes and pumping out the entrapped waters. The land is washed of its salts and the acres may not be ready for occupancy until twenty years after a particular polder-project is started. Nevertheless, at the beginning of each reclamation-project, the government plans for the total polder-community even to the sort of family unit best suited to occupy the farmlands extracted from the sea. They plan for the crops and their harvest, for the homes and schools, and for corollary services the anticipated community would require. Above all, they plan for balance. Most often they succeed admirably. More than half a million incredibly rich acres have already been reclaimed in these polder — and Holland is only one-tenth the size of California and one-fourth the size of New York. It is significant that more than 90 percent of Holland's land is owned in holdings of less than 50 acres, and some 50 percent in holdings of less than 10 acres.

By contrast, a Western American farmer needs some five acres merely for the storage of mechanized equipment. More than 50 percent of California famers own farm machinery valued at between $25,000 and $75,000; and fewer than 5 percent own less than $10,000 worth of mechanized equipment.

What sort of relationship can the equipment-farmer have with the land as he moves from area to area, mining as he would a mineral claim? What sort of planning for the future can one expect from this barren relationship? How can one compare this sort of agri-business with the Dutch form of balance, not only in terms of sustained yield and the renewing of resources but especially in terms of the inter-relationship of man with his Earth and with himself as an Earth-resource?

It was unavoidable that the mechanical ingenuity in which we take such pride should find a challenge in the geographic vastness of this country. The mechanical revolution in agriculture continues to stimulate the scientific revolution in agriculture. Both, inter-related, are somewhat haphazard.

For example: Tomatoes do not mature uniformly at the same time and are therefore hand-picked over a period of several months. Any number of devices have been invented to harvest tomatoes mechanically, but these automatic pickers

will remain experimental until plant-geneticists have uncovered a usable canning-tomato variety that will mature
uniformly. The probabilities are that such a variety will be
commercially available in the near future. The probabilities
also are that such scientific and mechanical advances will not
lower the price the consumer pays for a can of tomatoes,
since the cost of tomatoes contained in the standard can is
around one penny. Yet the drive for accelerated agricultural
mechanization consumes so much of our national energies.

Of course, mechanized tomato-picking will permit the
concentration of tomato-land holdings and release landown-
ers from the pressures created by the need for human pickers.
One wonders if such land-concentration throughout the entire agricultural complex and the concomitant removal of
farm workers from the land is the basic intent of our planners. If this is so, then our seemingly erratic farm policies
have a pattern of disturbing implications.

Since all equipment is costly, the small-farm owner cannot buy proper equipment to farm efficiently. Furthermore,
most such equipment is not designed for small farms and
little effort is being devoted to the development of small-
farm equipment since small farms are gradually being absorbed by the expanding ones. If the small-farm owner wants
to operate with rented modern equipment, he soon finds himself in the position of a landowner who is no more than a
sharecropper depending upon other people for his planting
and harvesting capacity. Of course, the wealthy farmers and
farm complexes can buy costly equipment. They can also
buy or lease more land for the maximum use of such equipment. Furthermore, they can and do encourage the design
and construction of still more expensive equipment against
which the small-farm owner can never hope to compete. This
situation readily lends itself to malignant spreading and to
an expanding and tightening spiral entrapping us all and
stunting our growth.

The corporate structures rising from the wealth of our land increasingly shape the complexion of agricultural purpose. While the number of farmers decreases, land-interest vested in fewer hands is financially stronger than it ever was in our country.

Farm co-operatives exert some restraint on random growth but they, too, have assumed many of the aspects of corporate structures. There are more similarities than differences among farm corporations, communes, and co-operatives. In all of these, man's relationship with the growing earth is increasingly impersonal and distant, and all attempt to compensate for this by increasing volume.

In our country numerous erratic attempts have been made to wrest order out of chaos, with the unhappy result of compounding the chaos. A revealing example of this is what happened, and continues to happen, in the cling peach industry.

Almost all clingstone peaches are used for canning purposes. Most of the world's supply is grown in the United States, and almost all of it in Northern California. During the Depression of the Thirties, cling-peach orchardists received as little as $6 a ton for their crop. Today they receive around $60 a ton.

Because of the uniqueness of this crop to the United States, and its limitation to a small area of California, the growers and processors, in cooperation with various government agencies, were able to agree to certain restrictive measures that would help stabilize the industry. It was a notable attempt observed with increasing interest by farm groups all over the world, many of whom sent commissions to California to study this operation.

What finally emerged and is presently functioning in the cling-peach industry is a marketing arrangement between growers and processors. An advisory board, consisting mainly of grower and processor representatives, agrees as to the quantity of peaches to be harvested, the grades that are acceptable, and the price the processors will pay to the growers for the crop. This advisory board collects a levy from each ton of peaches — a rather substantial annual sum which it uses for its own functions and for the stimulation of cling-peach sales. The industry is relatively stable and everyone seems to be quite content about it. This planning attempt has been held up as a model for other areas of agriculture to emulate, demonstrating how private enterprise, with only slim government assistance, can stabilize an industry and benefit both grower and processor.

However, there are many peculiarities here. The advisory board has legal authority over every bearing cling-peach tree growing in California. The board, representing grower and processor, estimates how many peaches will be purchased by consumers, and then dictates the size of the crop that will be purchased for processing. Since the crop is almost always greater than the cannery pack, the board has the authority to order the surplus peaches destroyed. The destruction of these surplus peaches — often amounting to tens of thousands of tons representing sometimes as much as 30 percent of the total crop — is meticulously executed. Growers are instructed to green-drop a percentage of the crop, and processors are instructed to divert a percentage of peaches that are in their possession and ready for processing.

In green-dropping, as it is called, the grower employs pickers to pull immature peaches off the trees so that they will not ripen. In cannery-diversion, as it is called, the harvested ripe peaches are quite literally garbaged. These are precisely the same sort of peaches, in terms of variety and quality, that go into the cans purchased by consumers. Green-dropping and cannery-diversion are costly operations, but the industry finds them necessary in order to maintain price stability. Moreover, the industry has the authority to destroy part of its crop whenever it believes its price structure to be threatened. Whenever the question is raised that perhaps a price reduction to the consumer of canned peaches will expand the demand for the crop, the industry refers to its mass of data collected by marketing-research experts that demonstrates that the economy can absorb only a given tonnage of canned cling peaches, and that a price reduction per can will not increase demand.

While the advisory board has control over every bearing cling-peach tree in California, it has no control over the number of acres anyone wants to plant to this crop. Such control would be overt interference with agricultural free enterprise. Destruction of part of the immature crop and garbaging of part of the edible crop is considered planning for economic stability, and carries with it the blessing of the government.

There are scores of similar idiocies throughout the entire spectrum of the agricultural complex. If these idiocies bloomed from an overdose of fecundity, let us devote our skills to avoid repeating them in the future. If these are not idiocies, but a planned approach to the wealth of the land, let us at least be aware of the vortex into which we are being swept.

It has become a political vogue to state that our farm problem is too complex for solution; that we should simply adapt ourselves to live with these complexities as acquiescently as possible; that the Earth is really too complicated by human and physical vagaries for us to do much about it; and that we should therefore devote our energies to a really concerted effort to reach the moon.

The complexity of our farm problem will continue to grow like Johnson grass in river-bottom soil because it stems basically from our undefined concept of what the Earth means to us, from our historic resentment at considering ourselves another one of Nature's resources, and from our failure to recognize and appreciate those factors of renewability which reside only in the individual.

We must evaluate the purpose of bigness. We must recognize that bigness does not mean greatness. We must certainly attempt to define, as clearly as we can, our inter-relationship with all of Nature within which we are indivisible.

(April 30, 1961)

XIII

The Angle of Divergence

WHETHER MAN CAN or cannot escape his fate is rhetorical; he certainly cannot escape his environment since he, as well as every other organism and object in nature, is an inescapable part of, and constantly enveloped by, his environment.

However, because he is capable of saying anything that can be said, man can alter his environment even unto sterility by untruths. This capability need bear no relationship whatever to the value of what he says. Only man, in all of nature, is capable of untruths that can actually alter his inter-relationship with his total environment.

These untruths may be deliberate. They may even be factors of national purpose, as with the Aryan concepts that enveloped so much of the world. They may be the results of unforgivable omissions of wisdom from the calculations and

hurried projections of those gentle individuals in whom the
people of the world believed wisdom resided — as with Einstein, Bohr, and other nuclear pathfinders of our age.

When seeds of untruth are planted in the barren soil of an
acquiescent society, a harvest of confusion seems to be inevitable. If these seeds are also fertilized by virulent excretions
of gangrenous minds, the stench of decay can asphyxiate
mankind.

It is precisely because man's untruths can alter his inter-
relationship with his total environment that personal discernment by the individual, for himself, becomes continuously
essential for his function and survival. While this was always
so, individual discernment has never been a more critical need
for man than it is today when so much scientific capability
bears so little relationship to value, to the acquisition and
preservation of individual dignity.

In all of nature, harmful bacteria represent only a minute
fraction of the total bacterial population; noxious plants are
actually quite rare; poisonous snakes are many times out-
numbered by nonharmful reptiles; even among the human
young, while delinquency may arrest public attention, it is
statistically infrequent. In science, however, projects intimately related to destruction are far more prevalent, more
pampered, and more publicly honored than projects related
to nondestruction. Throughout history scientific objectivity
has been a quest for knowledge. Today it is a hurried search
for destruction. Are we to assume that knowledge and destruction are synonymous in science? Why could this angle
of divergence, so crudely askew today, stretch its arms with
such thrust as to encompass an acquiescent society? Probably because individual discernment was clouded by dependence upon others in whom wisdom was expected.

A minute angle of divergence may be unrecognized at the
point of origin where the arms touch. Discernment of the
angle is sharpened as the arms stretch from the point of

contact. If the arms thrust increasingly forward, the distance between them inevitably widens until they seem unrelated to one another; and the arms are unrecognized as stemming from the same point of origin, now too distant on the horizon for recall.

When the gentle theoreticians germinated the seed that later exploded, they showed little wisdom — not because the explosion enveloped man in a permanent cloud which irreversibly altered his ecology, but because they created an angle of divergence in science, the arms of which are so far apart today as to be almost beyond recall or even recognition. They performed the surgery that altered the course of science from a quest for knowledge to a search for destruction; and they helped to reduce the stature of man to the present point where he accepts sterility as potential fecundity.

This angle of divergence has so traduced science that one of its arms stirs up hurricanes of destruction in every segment of man's striving while massed mankind is seduced into believing itself touched by the gentle zephyrs of a new springtime.

The gentle theoreticians were certainly aware of this angle of divergence. What then did they anticipate when, with such monumental striving, they unleashed the beast upon the world from their uncomfortable minds? Did they expect their disciples to tame it when they themselves offered no guidance?

The intent here is not to lament the doom of man by science.

Factors of divergence apply not only to science but to each of us in every facet of our daily lives. The individual who cannot find and will not seek discernment within himself permits himself to be enticed to his slaughter in the happy belief that the concrete bunker to which he is being led is his new Temple of Refuge, when actually it is the killing floor of the abattoir. Such an individual seems to be going where he is going quite willingly — even hopefully. If along his path realities are hidden under the creeping vines of scientific absurdity, he picks a tendril to crown his head with a hero's wreath.

So much of science has an emphasis which can only be considered absurd. For example, one part of the world exults when a cosmonaut orbits the Earth and part of the world is depressed because this cosmonaut is not theirs. Exultation and depression accruing simultaneously from the same fact. Who speaks for the totality of man in this regard?

Orbital flight is an absurd emphasis of science at this point in man's time on Earth. We possess scientific resources and vast quantities of knowledge; but these are overshadowed by vaster problems and broader ignorance. If orbital fllight resulted from science's quest for knowledge mankind could, with honor, exult. But all orbital flight, whether from the East or the West, is the direct result of the search of science for destruction.

What are the aims of science today? What weights and orders of preference are assigned to these objectives? There are none. National science is governed by emotion instead of by reason. Never before in history has there been such a universal acceptance of a single concept — the tortured belief in Science as the hope of man.

How far askew has science gone from the point of origin of its angle of divergence? Much too far; almost beyond the point of recall.

The life-supporting land is itself being forked by this same angle of divergence.

Every person on Earth is directly and daily affected by the land and what it produces; this has been so since man's beginnings. Probably one of the first applications of ancient man's intelligence was to the soil from which he sought and found sustenance. All past cultures independently evolved an almost mystic relationship between man and his Earth. When a nation, to repel an invader, scorched its earth to starve its enemy, mankind gasped in awe at such sacrifice.

Throughout the world science is now evolving a new concept toward the life-supporting soil and what it produces. This concept, actively pursued in both East and West, demonstrates how far askew science has gone from its angle of divergence, and poses a threat to whatever sanity remains on Earth.

Not-so-gentle theoreticians, working for government, seem to have decided that the next phase in weaponry could well be agricultural warfare, requiring neither nuclear bombs nor expensive missiles; neither armies, navies, nor air forces but only the utter corruption of science in conjunction with a thoroughly acquiescent society.

The thought of these government-scientists is that any enemy could be vanquished through an undeclared and almost undetectable strategy of starvation, which would not kill the enemy or destroy his industrial capacity. It would be nearly impossible to determine who started the attack, or when it was started. Crop-killing insects and microbes, selected and made more virulent by scientists, would be launched secretly against an enemy country. Small quantities of inoculum, undetectably carried by individuals, could readily be spread in the designated areas of the target country. For a year or two the inoculated areas would remain fairly dormant; and then the disease would become virulent and widespread. If conditions were ripe, millions of acres of crops could be destroyed without the target country knowing whether to blame natural causes or enemy action for their crop failures. Meanwhile, during the time between inoculation and devastation, the disease-spreading nation could divert the world, including its enemy, with pious assurances.

Agricultural scientists in the East and the West are presently working on such projects.

Scientists of the U.S.A. have found ways to develop new kinds of plant diseases which, they maintain in published reports, could quickly lay waste millions of acres of wheat, rice, and potatoes, the chief staples in many communist lands.

Russian scientists have succeeded in breeding a type of blackstem rust to which wheat in the U.S.A. is extremely susceptible.

Two Polish scientists in mid-1961 published a treatise in which they commented: "In the United States alone, the destruction of grain and other agricultural crops causes an annual damage estimated at billions of dollars. But all this is 'peaceful' action — crop diseases and pests spread spontaneously. What would happen if similar factors were to be used under military conditions?"

A U.S. Government agricultural scientist stated that mysterious new outbreaks of crop and animal diseases around the world, along with persistent attacks by longer-established pests, are of grave concern to our researchers. While we have no evidence to show that any of these outbreaks are being caused deliberately, he said, we have nothing to prove that they are accidental; and, therefore, we need a budget and a plan to prepare ourselves for any eventuality.

Numerous similar excretions are stemming from scientists in the East and the West. A country's crop failures can no longer be blamed on natural phenomena; or improperly planned agricultural practices; or indiscriminate applications of technical policies toward the land; or land-debilitating commune concepts (whether they be the people-commune concepts of the East or the finance-commune concepts of the West); or on avarice; or on man's having so altered his environment to the point of rejection. Crop failures are now suspect. Behind them could lurk the science of the enemy.

When scientists are asked whether this particular application of their knowledge does not make them feel corrupted, the reply is, usually, that all types of warfare are immoral, but that all this is really not any of their doing.

Parenthetically, two Australian medical scientists reported early in 1961 that they found that constant exposure to insecticides derived from deadly nerve gases, such as parathion and malathion, brings on symptoms of psychiatric disorder. Parathion and malathion are very heavily used in this country, next in volume to DDT; and agricultural research people here have long been familiar with this occupational hazard and side-effect. However, the insanity of the theoreticians who ponder unleashing agricultural warfare does not originate from parathion or malathion, but from the angle of divergence all of science suffered two decades ago.

DDT, as an example, has been hailed as a major advance in agriculture and public health and its use has become widespread and indiscriminate. It is now becoming recognized as a major hazard to humans, and the government has forbidden the interstate shipment of milk containing traces of DDT since, once ingested, DDT remains in the body harmfully and indefinitely. Under rigid control-conditions DDT may be a useful tool in man's arsenal for his conquest of the planet; however, its present improper and indiscriminate use is so altering Earth's bio-ecology that its threat to animal-life in North America, for example, is greater than deforestation, drought, or any combination of decimating causes.

For more than 95 percent of the world's population, cereal grains are the main source of food energy. Probably more effort has been expended for cereal crop research than for any other aspect of agriculture. Yet today, in this country and throughout the world, heretofore resistant strains of cereals are being wiped out by new strains of pathogens — disease-carrying organisms — to which the host-cereals are not resistant.

Nature, without modification by scientists, can put virulence into pathogens much more rapidly than scientists can put genetic resistance into crop plants. Wheat alone can be attacked by any of the more than 300 known varieties of wheat-rust disease. Even when resistant strains of crops are developed, we have no assurance that the strain will remain resistant for any length of time. We know little about the nature of resistance — and less about its genetics. In 1953, in the Plains States of our broad country, farmers planted the best varieties of oats that geneticists had been able to develop in some thirty years of breeding for rust-resistance; yet that year, it was reported that oat-rust disease caused more severe yield-reductions than at any time in the history of that vast area.

Why?

We do not know.

When so much knowledge remains elusive, to devote national energies, as a matter of national policy, to deliberate man-made crop annihilation is a corruption of a science and a pollution of all mankind. This would be so even if there was not so much hunger relentlessly increasing throughout the world.

Quite realistically, the arm of angle of divergence can be extended even further. For example, most people throughout the world use tobacco. In most countries tobacco products are a government monopoly. Even where cigarettes and other such products are not a government monopoly, only a handful of private companies is involved. It is scientifically feasible for governments to introduce surreptitiously certain drugs into tobacco products which would depress the mass of its people into acquiescence while the chosen few would be supplied from a private bin. Soft drinks, made of secret formulas, spill out of this country in sufficient volume to dampen much of the world. It would be no great scientific feat to add acquiescence-producing drugs to these drinks and thereby soften an enemy for conquest.

To paraphrase the agricultural scientist mentioned earlier, there is no proof that this is being done; but neither is there proof that this is not being done. All of which is reminiscent of the archaeologist who dug through ancient ruins and, finding no wires, announced to the world his proof that this ancient society therefore possessed wireless.

There are no limits to the whirls of idiocy contained in such a spiral of scientific absurdity.

And through all this haze of the half-truths wends the polluted stream of personal and public acquiescence by individuals who cannot find and will not seek within themselves discernment of their inter-relationship with their total environment.

Wherever the land is husbanded through people-communes or finance-communes, the individual's comprehension of his life-supporting Earth recedes; and with it, part of himself is given into the safekeeping of others.

In our own country the vast land-mass of America was at one time a challenge to man in his eternal translation of the wealth of the land into human use. So much of America first felt the effects of man's acceleration through his mechanical extensions. In this hasty and unexplored exchange of machine for man we have lost something irreplaceable from our heritage of values and purpose. We have had no period of transition between exploring and exploiting during which to evolve any sort of conceptual approach to the richness of our land. Now there seems to be an impersonal and barren relationship between the people and the life-supporting Earth.

We like to think of our country as the wealthiest of food nations and as a living prophesy of continuing plenty; yet we have no philosophy of agriculture from which we might reap guidance for the continuation of plenty. Instead, weeds of indecision, enriched by avarice, bring forth harvests of confusion affecting all people — farming and nonfarming — and dissipating our strength before nations.

When the non-farm dweller remains ignorant of his relationship to the land he encourages the growth of concepts that permit exploitation of the land. These same concepts inevitably reach out to exploit him.

This seems to be valid for all peoples, in the West as well as in the East.

Throughout the world we now find science — historic guardian of reason — kneeling before emotion in order to receive accolades from a society it has helped to make benighted.

There is nothing wrong with emotion. Perhaps emotion without reason may be biology; and reason without emotion may be sterility; however, specious reasoning coupled with spurious emotion is surely abortive.

The individual confronts the wall of emotion many times during his life; certainly when he first recognizes his personal beginnings and as he later approaches his own termination. So often this wall of emotion presses against all of us so that we mumble, with near-incomprehension, the jumbled rituals of our personal history. Do we mumble in our beginning because we have no words, and near our termination because we have no hope?

In a world constricted by emotional science, the incomprehensive mumblings generate a dulled agony in those whose ears strain to hear a clear hope expressed with dignity and with a scope encompassing all mankind.

Reason pushes this wall of emotion away from us so that we can hear ourselves and others — so that we can take a clean breath without constriction. Only reason can move back this wall of emotion to give us personal scope within which we can find ourselves and our place in nature — scope in which we can, if we so wish, stretch our arms in an attempt to embrace the world. After achievement of personal scope, perhaps we can mount the wall of emotion and use it as an observation point from which to scan the measure of our days on Earth.

This is not a lamentation over the totality of science, so much of which has benefited mankind, even as so many of the total varieties of micro-organisms benefit mankind. It is a condemnation of those who form the segments of science that are the virulent centers of infections capable of destroying, as well as themselves, the host, mankind. We have no built-in genetic resistance to these infections; yet we seem to coddle the infectors and the infections with a strange sort of hypochondria.

Einstein was a great and noble man, as were many of his colleagues; but when the wall of emotion pressed against him, he, too, fumbled; and the edifice of man, to whose construction he and his colleagues devoted so much of their earlier efforts, began to show the cracks and faulting of that angle of divergence their emotions had helped to draw.

The search for destruction would probably have been pursued vigorously and successfully by others. Did these gentle theoreticians merely accelerate the search? Perhaps. Could they have stopped the search for destruction? Unquestionably, no.

What could they have done?

They could have projected, with wisdom, factors of inevitability. They could have struggled more mightily than they did against the angle of divergence that has so quickly corrupted science into a massive worldwide search for threat.

They could have studied their project's paragenesis: the formation of inorganic materials in contact so as to affect one another's development; and its schizogenesis: its biologic reproduction by fission. They could have pondered the ecology of their seed and offspring and the inter-relationship with their total environment. If they had done these things, then with wisdom they could have brought to bear upon the future of man the full weight of their greatness and nobility, and mankind would not be enveloped today in a moral fallout even more cumulative than the radioactive fallout they accelerated.

In the convolutions of the minds of these gentle theoreticians their hope probably turned toward their disciples.

Two decades later, after almost a generation of gestation, that hope seems even more barren than Marie Antionette's pregnancy, recorded in history as a gust of wind.

If the question of whether man can or cannot escape his fate is unquestionably rhetorical, the point, then, is that he certainly cannot escape his environment, which he constantly alters.

Whether man alters his environment unto sterility or fecundity depends not only upon the scientists but upon the personal discernment of the individual, each according to his own capacity, as it is stimulated by his personal awareness of himself as a total human being, and as the universe-in-miniature.

(August 11, 1961)

XIV

The Anathema of the Unknown

MAN'S RECOGNITION AND acceptance of himself as a total human being is increasingly essential for sanity in an increasingly complex world. Attempts to expand comprehension of his environment expand the individual's horizons and offer him personal scope within which he can stand erect. Deliberately or tacitly limiting or rejecting comprehension of his environment contracts the individual to his knees — not in supplication, but because of near stifling in the close prison of his own physical and mental waste.

The unity of man as a total organism has never been a philosophic concept in science. Science is concerned essentially with measurable phenomena, and a measure for the unity of man has never before been within the grasp of man.

Religious philosophies emerging from common antiquity into Eastern and Western convolutions are devoted essentially to the non-measurable aspects of man. In his ascent toward comprehension of himself, man is confronted by the barrier of immeasurability of his place in nature. Bruising himself against this barrier, he has throughout history sought refuge in various philosophies of faith where measurements are neither necessary nor desired.

While X-the-unknown is anathema to science, which continually attempts to expose its characteristics, the unknown is cherished by religion; and the unknown itself is identified by religion as the plan for, and purpose of, man.

Individuals have always existed among those who could not truly cherish the unknown as their purpose in life, and who, through their arts and abilities, have tried to create bridges of comprehension between measurability and immeasurability, knowledge and faith.

Most scientists have always recognized the finiteness — the limitation — of knowledge. Belief, however, is limitless; one can believe anything one wants to, just as one can say anything capable of being said. Truth and belief need not be related. Since belief can neither be proved nor disproved, it often has a rather tenuous relationship to knowledge.

Yet belief may be true, and knowledge may be inaccurate or incomplete.

Many scientists are now searching their souls, pondering whether science can enrich religious beliefs, and whether religion can ennoble the scientific search for knowledge. Throughout much of their search wends a thread of guilt and confessional as though they now recognize their own roles in turning science into something not completely to be trusted. Neither can they trust traditional beliefs. In their search for bits and pieces — for fragments — so many of which are aimed against mankind and themselves, they have abdicated their responsibilities toward their fellowman and now find themselves orphaned.

This seems to be especially so among many of the pre-atomic-age scientists whose prior atmosphere of peaceful objectivity has been shattered. They now seek purpose with which they can identify themselves in the administration of the universe; a sense of belonging to a whole that is greater than the sum of their own parts; a source of reason, explanation, comfort, and warmth in a world grown cold. Actually, we all seek these assurances in our attempts to find meaning and purpose in ourselves and our society.

It is the contention here that the seeking of purpose in the administration of the universe is a misdirected quest of no value if we do not recognize that man — here and now and for as long as he survives — is the universe-in-miniature. If we can uncover man's purpose in the administration of his own life, family, society, and world, we may then be able to comprehend the universe. If our ability toward comprehension of ourselves continues to be limited, if our desires toward such comprehension are corrupted through disregard for our fellowman and our world, we continue in ignorance of ourselves and of our universe.

If our abilities toward comprehension are limited, while we expand our abilities toward total destruction, we will eventually annihilate ourselves through built-in and unavoidable accident-probabilities. This country possesses stockpiled nuclear weaponry of some tens of thousands of times the power of the bomb that cremated Hiroshima, and it is constantly adding to this stockpile. The U.S.S.R. probably has an equivalent stockpile. England and France probably have smaller but quite measurable stockpiles. Unquestionably, China will soon have her own nuclear weaponry and her own substantial stockpile; and so, probably, will other governments as the cost of producing basic nuclear weaponry steadily declines with expanding technology.

Since no device ever constructed is completely fool-proof, accident probabilities within these stockpiles steadily increase. Electronic computers used in the manufacture, control, and disposition of these stockpiles are certainly not fool-proof, and their absolute efficiency leaves much to be desired. Even the massive computer-complexes used in satellite programs now need second-stage computers to check out the primary ones; and perhaps third-stage devices will be needed to check the checkers. Computer authorities agree that with so much electronic equipment, malfunction is to be expected occasionally as a matter of normal procedure.

Can we afford even an occasional malfunction in the world's stockpile of nuclear weaponry? If our abilities toward comprehension are as limited as they appear to be, we must expect the accident as a matter of normal procedure. If our desires toward comprehension are corrupted, total erasure of man on his planet is, of course, unavoidable.

In this context the scientists' search for purpose in the administration of the universe is without meaning unless we first explore and determine man's purpose in the administration of himself, on his own planet.

If we are part of a two billion or four billion light-year expanse, each man is to himself the center of this universe, the focal point of reference to all this vastness, to all things near and far, to all time in the past, present, and conceivable future. And out of the millions or billions of possible man-like habitable planets our Earth is the focal point of reference.

Enveloped by it, living in it, drawing life from it, we call it "home" and take it for granted; and after a while we scarcely notice it at all. Only the children and those few adults who are still fresh enough to wonder about the big and little things in their world are able to look around and see the daily wonder of our home and planet belonging to them — a heritage from the past through the present and into a future, as Nature's bounty, to be used wisely and well.

We often tend to think of our Earth as motionless. It is often quiet but never still. It grows and decays; and each day, for us, a little is reborn and a little more dies. Our Earth land-mass is some 36 billion acres. How can anyone feel personal toward something so vast? Yet when compared to a billion light-year universe, our Earth is smaller than a hummingbird's wingtip against the mountain-barrage of all the Rockies.

This is our Earth, in our universe; and we really have not done very well by it or toward ourselves.

Science, striving to scale the barrier between man's hope and his grasp of his place in nature, drills toe holds that are inadequate to sustain his full weight, precisely because a conceptual basis for the unity of man has never before existed in science.

Science is essentially segmented. Man, basically, is not.

However, despite segmentation, science has now achieved a theoretically measurable unity toward all of mankind. This theoretical measure, never before in existence, affords a least common denominator that can apply with equal validity to all of mankind. The reference here is to the theoretical possibility of the total annihilation of Man on Earth. For the first time in history science has achieved a theoretical measure for the unity of man. That this measure is universal man-made death is unpalatable — but factual and undeniable.

That man hopes to retain life by threatening death to others and to himself is a cosmic absurdity. The use of this absurdity as a hothouse for the germination of national and international policies is an indication of mankind's accelerated removal from sanity. Every segment of life throughout the world is affected by this absurdity; and the quiet horror is that we are accepting and learning to live with it.

The point here is not that man is being doomed by his devices; or by his learning to control his machines or compete against them. A competitor invariably assumes some of the characteristics of the subject of his competition — and no one truly wants to become mechanized.

The point is that the unity of man can now become a philosophic concept in science; and if mankind is to survive, it must inevitably become such a concept and science will have to measure itself against the base line of man's unity. That which strengthens the unity of man will be worthy of the name of science; that which increasingly threatens and segments man, placing him in undignified competition with his machines, will then be condemned as a corruption both of science and of mankind.

Would such condemnation have any effect at all?

Possibly. No one today — in Germany or elsewhere — publicly extols the scientific innovations of the Nazi crematoria. Not all of the note books of the Nazi scientists detailing bestial experiments on death-camp prisoners have been destroyed. While many are undoubtedly cherished by corrupt scientists as a sort of scientific pornography, even these men hesitate to make their possessions known for fear of public revulsion. Public revulsion is still a powerful restraint; it is perhaps the only remaining public restraint.

Within the time of recorded history men have fought for the salvation not of their own souls, which they considered safe for all time, but for the souls of strangers. They mounted Holy Crusades, Holy Wars, and Holy Inquisitions against those who did not believe as they believed. These warriors in the battles for men's souls were true believers when they offered their misdirected enemies the choice of being saved or of dying. These men of the Holy Death were not all beasts; yet we look down history upon them as crude and cruel examples of man's inhumanity and immaturity.

Today the warriors of the world, engaged in a battle for men's minds, mount Holy Crusades, Holy Wars, and Holy Inquisitions against those who do not believe as they believe. These men of the Unholy Threat are not all beasts. Many are true believers, with a faith as deadly as any of their forebears who pierced an infidel's heart with a lance blessed in ritual by his God's self-chosen representatives. Will future history look down upon these men as crude and cruel examples of man's inhumanity and immaturity? Probably so, if there is history.

Are we free-falling through space with no parachute and no guidance-system for our own self-recovery?

We seem to be doing precisely that — perhaps not out of malice or corruption — but certainly because we have encouraged limits toward the comprehension of the individual and his society. Except as a statistic, the individual is not given much importance in the accidents of the world. If the numbers of people involved are large enough, we can be shocked. When one flying aircraft plows into another and a hundred or more dying individuals hurtle to the ground in a shower of human and metallic debris, the headlines of the world grasp and reflect our momentary horror.

When we think of nuclear devices it is in terms of the hundreds of thousands and millions of people that can be destroyed. Yet each man lives his own life and dies his own death. The dignity and value of the individual has become almost incomprehensible in a world where the U.S.A. and the U.S.S.R. each possess stockpiles of nuclear weaponry equivalent to hundreds or thousands of pounds of death for every human being on our planet. And we keep adding to our stockpile, even as other countries keep adding to theirs.

Certainly, to other intelligences on other plants in our universe, this would seem the height of insanity; yet we are learning to live with this. Is it because we seem to have no choice or because we have a dulled ability to relate facts and ideas to individuals? Perhaps.

Every 24 hours the world's scientific community prints millions of words in their reports. How much of this relates to the dignity and value of the individual? Of course we live in a society becoming increasingly complex where our dependence upon devices increases daily. Breakdowns in these devices must be expected as a matter of normal procedure. Printed manuals do not, however, always expedite repair.

And in all our masses of data and complexities of equipment, within which the individual has become a statistical unit of a statistical mass, there is no guidance system for our own self-recovery.

It is the contention here that man is responsible and must hold himself to account for his own actions. This is his authority and his value. If the man happens to be a scientist, and his actions are for the benefit or detriment of himself and his fellowman, he too must be held to account, by himself and by his fellowman.

Yet so many of us surrender without struggle or honor to self-dilution and to the denial of our value as individuals by abdicating to those who direct our lives with gadgetry and jargon, cynicism and ignorance. If the individual tried to expand his personal comprehension of his ecology there would be no surrender. However, if the individual is anxious or willing to accept contentment as his goal and mass-man as his place in nature, his surrender seems as unavoidable as his conformity, which is the basic ingredient of mass-man. For mass-man there is neither threat nor promise, merely existence as an undifferentiated particle, prey to the whims of undistinguishable leaders and undistinguishable science.

Man is now measurably united in terms of his theoretical annihilation. This is what science has accomplished. All the philosophies of faith have not been able to unite mankind.

Can science, with new concept of unity, eliminate threat and strive toward promise? This is one of the basic questions of our time. As an emerging science, the Ecology of Man is devoted to and concerned with the inter-relationship of man as a total human being with his total environment. The Ecology of Man, therefore, holds the greatest promise for the solution of the basic questions of our time.

Science generally continues to shed light on many segments of man's aspirations. However, merely to shed light is not sufficient. The brilliance of a powerful searchlight turned on Broadway at bright noon is certainly less illuminating than a pencil-thin light probing a darkened corner. The brightness of the light cast on particular areas often deepens the shadows of adjacent areas. Lights searching in wrong places are ineffective and wasteful, offering a false sense of awareness and accomplishment.

There is an inter-relationship between indiscriminate growth and confusion. We are in the midst of a second scientific revolution which began with the bomb blast at Alamagordo — a massive exclamation point ending the first scientific revolution that began more than two hundred years before. Hopefully we may yet have a third scientific revolution of considerably greater value than the first two. This second revolution, still in ferment, has been as swift and indiscriminate as the bomb. Within it we are still constricted by the nature of simultaneity and immediacy. While we seek water from the sea, we must also seek solutions for population pressures and for the thousands of other emergences from Pandora's Box. Problems are now generated with greater rapidity and in greater complexity than solutions, since each attempted solution seems to expose ever-increasing problems.

This second revolution, with little wisdom present at its core, and with depleted opportunities for the individual to

grasp the full measure of his days on Earth, continues to
generate fear and confusion. Rashly we rush from nuclear
bombs to nuclear reactors without fully comprehending
even the problems of nuclear waste-disposal. We hasten
from electronic devices to automated equipment without
grasping the nature of man's relationship to his machines.
We try to escape population-explosions by crawling into
country-slum subdivisions without pausing to wonder what
all this does to our water and pollution problems and to the
social stratification now taking place in our society.

Are the Untouchables in our society those individuals
who resist absorption into mass-man? Despite gadgetry and
our vaunted electronic ease we seem to be in constant ferment, constantly subjected to the crudities of new emergences from our material fecundity. We scarcely have time
to ponder the nature of man-made promise or man-made
threat before we are inundated by more promise and newer
threat. We are in an age of seeming material plenty and
obvious personal uncertainty — an age of intricate and skillful
communications networks coursing the world and decreasing
comprehension between peoples and nations. Even within
the family-unit, one member seldom comprehends another.
We are in an age of constant separations and segmentations;
of unpalatable moon-shot projects and less palatable defense-
stockpiles; of almost undecipherable hieroglyphics in terms
of the dignity and value of the individual. And over it all
hovers the threat, the constant theoretical threat, of total
annihilation, the only unity of mankind that has some scientific measure. Measurable quantities of thermonuclear stockpiles, man-made in the East or the West, can explode the
planet. There are no Eastern or Western convolutions emerging from this common measure.

Are we then to assume that man must face threat in order
to function? That he cannot move forward unless he is

pushed from behind? Animals are often that way, but man need not be so unless he collaborates in his own enmassment.

It is now stylish to believe the behavioral sciences are the keys to unlock man's understanding of himself and dispel confusion and misdirection.

The behavioral sciences are those segments of inquiry involved with why man behaves as he does. Psychology, psychiatry, motivational research, and other such segmented skills belong to the behavioral sciences. Their broad intent is to find out why people feel destructive toward themselves and each other and then do something about it. If we can find out why we behave as we do, we can then be led away with gentle proddings from destructive channels into constructive ones.

But who is to guide whom? Who is to research the behavioral researchers?

The basic question of our time remains: Can all of science, with the terminal realism of its new concept of unity, eliminate threat and strive toward promise? The problem of deciphering the hieroglyphics of this nuclear age is rather straightforward. Scientists, many of whom are also individuals, must recognize their responsibility toward strengthening the unity of mankind. Any projects that fragment man should be recognized as scientific irresponsibility. If, in order to strengthen this unity, scientists must begin to eliminate from their thinking previously ingested doctrines that this planet is a grouping of geographic fragments and that man is a grouping of fragmented responses, it is certainly time they did so.

Since we now possess techniques enabling us to scale the barrier separating man's hope from the grasp of his place in nature, we need no longer bruise ourselves against the barrier of immeasurability. We are presently in the midst of scientific anarchy and near-insanity from which we shall either extricate ourselves by ourselves — or perish.

And we can extricate ourselves only through the direct recognition, each according to his capacity, of his individual dignity and of the unity of all mankind.

(July 28, 1961)

XV

Promise Coupled to Threat

In THIS SECOND half of the Twentieth Century our world is unequally divided — not nearly so much by East and West as by our receding past and our mushrooming present. The hard core of our history is fading — not because it is so far behind us, but because our present glitter blinds us even as it envelopes us in a deep and forbidding shadow. On our world platform, nakedly spotlighted, a juvenile chorus of loud threat beats against our minds with obscene rhythm, while we, the audience, pinioned to our seats, writhe in the false heat of self-indulgence. The performers are there only because we, the audience, seduced by promise, paid an entrance-fee that is not returnable.

From the world's recently refined technical skills promise and threat have emerged simultaneously. The promise of abundance remains essentially unredeemed, while the threat from these skills continues to expand. Have we, then, without questioning, accepted the assumption that threat and promise are so joined that the removal of threat will shatter the promise?

We can ponder, perhaps with benefit, how all this came about so very quickly — in much less time than it takes a growing child to become father of his growing child.

There is a factor of inevitability here which possesses deep individual implications and responsibilities that needs to be recognized.

While any number of organisms in nature — including man — are capable of transmitting their material abundance from one generation to the next, man is the only organism in nature which is capable of transmitting patterns of acquired knowledge and values from one generation to the next.

The promise offered mankind by contemporary science and technique was one of material plenty; and we evolved the highest degree of technical skill the world has ever known for the acquisition of this tangible wealth. Every nation on Earth seeks to emulate the productive capacity of its richer protagonist or antagonist; and while the struggle may be labelled "the battle for men's minds," it is actually a statistical haggle for men's consumptive capacities as purchasers of this material plenty. Statistical addiction is a symptom of mental brittleness; and brittleness, unable to withstand pressure, shatters very quickly. When statistical addiction increases in a society exhausting itself of purpose, the evacuation of morality is hastened; and then, as whenever a vacuum is destroyed and the vessel containing it is shattered rather than pierced, the loudness of its destruction is directly related to the size of the vacuum and the impact of the shatterer.

It seems that today's science can neither promise, nor provide values by which men can guide their lives. Today's science can compound colors, but it cannot create the painting; it can design typewriters, but it cannot create the novel; it can construct instruments, but it cannot create music. Because of its nature, simultaneously containing promise and threat, today's science is either constructive or destructive but has ceased to be creative. Even in the quite recent past there was much philosophy in physics; today the statistical laws of physics encourage their own brittleness. The systematic compilation of instances for the inference of general truths, which is the basis of statistics, is so easily available today with our data-accumulation devices that the mass of data can, of itself, become restrictive.

Since only man can transmit values to his succeeding generations, what nonmaterial values can today's science from the East or the West offer as the legacy of our heritage to the future?

That equal fear equally shared is progress?

That promise and threat are so joined that the removal of threat will shatter the promise?

Future generations will scarcely cherish this concept as their inheritance from our generation containing, as it does, their first post-atomic-age ancestors.

In our tremendous expenditure of energy for the acquisition of material plenty, toward which all of mankind seems to yearn, we are left with too little energy for the discernment of values; and much too soon the need for values recedes from our conscious awareness. The encrustations normally deposited by the daily ebb-and-flow of living so frequently present debilitating removal-problems whenever we attempt to reach into the substance of our lives, in an effort to abstract the essence of our past for the guidance of our future.

Unhappily, today's science and technique cater to mankind's gluttony for those material acquisitions which have become manifestations of progress, even as mankind has become obese and insensitive to the refinements of transmittable value and personal future.

Today the choice is too often between acquiring a new automobile or a new idea; it seems that both cannot be secured simultaneously. Today the push-button mechanized ease for which we strive is so closely related to push-button destruction that in our hunger for one we accept the other. Why not? It is all part of the bargain-package, equally priced throughout the world. That so many of these purchases are not needed for continued existence and may actually endanger continued existence is scarcely given a passing thought.

For man, the less biologically necessary the acquisition, the more energy he expends to acquire it; and the more it is biologically necessary, the less thought and energy are required from man for its function. This can perhaps be called the natural law of human intensity and describes the direct inverse relationship existing between biologic need and human effort. The greater the biologic need, the less continuous effort is required for achievement; and the lesser the biologic need, the greater is the directed effort man expends for its achievement. The heart, for example, continues to beat even when the individual is asleep or unconscious; the cell-division within the toe does not depend upon the individual's conscious awareness of this vital biologic process, without which he could not continue to live. And in the pursuit of his strivings and passions — functions that are not biologically necessary for him — man expends vast reservoirs of his energy. This is true only of man, whose strivings and passions can quite actually consume him and his society.

Despite this destructive consumption, so little of man's science and skill is being devoted to the definition and comprehension of his strivings and his passions — the only ingredients from which transmittable values may emerge. Unhappily, so much of his energies are devoted to the acquisition of material plenty — which he then offers in his last will and testament as full measure of his days on Earth.

When, in bewildered lamentation, we ask ourselves how this age of scientific enlightenment could be laden with so much personal anxiety and shrouded in such dimness, we resist looking for the answer in the only place it could be found — within ourselves, our own households, and our own strivings.

If mechanized ease has truly given us increased leisure for the contemplation of our aspirations and the comprehension of our inter-relationship with our environment these mechanized extensions of ours would be subservient to us. But mechanized ease, itself, seems to be the goal; and wherever this is so, man becomes subservient to his mechanized extensions. Once this goal of ease is within man's reach, he feels himself rejected by and unrelated to his environment.

What has our nuclear age actually contributed to the moral concepts of our time? This deeply personal question can be asked only by the individual, for himself and for the identification of his own value.

So much of science and technique have spiced man's life with dim visions of distant places and distant hopes. But too much spice so perverts the palate that it ceases to function with discernment.

Science has quite actually stripped man of prior values and replaced them with none — with no values but the glistening raiment of a gaudy mirage. In his historic ascent from the cave man has often stumbled and then recovered to continue his climb; but today, if he stumbles, the downward path is greased for his return to the cave now being readied by all the skills of technique to embrace him as a permanent guest.

To accept the well-supplied and air-conditioned cave as man's greatest achievement in this age is clearly obscene.

If man has been stripped of his prior values, from what part of the race-memory of the species will new ones emerge? Since the old values have led us to our present dilemma, they are no longer valid; certainly they offer mankind no guidance or direction. And nobody ever returns, unchanged, to his point of departure.

Primitive societies were able to survive with primitive philosophies, primitive gods, and primitive aspirations. Our society is unutterably complex; we have made it so. Science demands that we follow factual evidence, that we use clear measurements. The metre is a clear measure, but not for weight; the pound is a clear measure, but not for distance. The mere possession of measurements is not sufficient; we must also know to what these measurements apply.

Today's science is not equipped to identify application; and without such identification our measurements are invalid.

We cannot visualize change if everything expands or contracts equally. If we expand precisely with our references, how can we measure this change? Measurement always requires stability in the observer. Even when the measurement-factors change, we must know previously the precise nature of this change. If we do not know, we could be in the opening eye of a hurricane, unaware of the calamitous winds by which we are surrounded and which can whirl us in one direction and then the other until we have lost all stability and all awareness has been wrenched from us.

The telescope is a remarkable instrument for the viewing of objects in space. Telescopes achieve such tremendous size that the viewing lens can be used only to cast light upon photographic plates, which are then studied at leisure with reference to prior exposures; and yet — regardless of the size of the light-collecting lens — the viewing lens, in the final application, must be small enough to fit the human eye. Furthermore, the object in space, the collecting and viewing lenses of the telescope, and the viewing eye must all be highly stable with reference to each other for meaningful measurements to be extracted. The platform upon which the telescope and viewing eye are placed, while rigidly stable to support man and machine, must be able to follow the object quite smoothly as it progresses through space, even as telescope and viewer themselves progress through space in accordance with the movements of Earth. If man and machine joggle, even simultaneously, the viewed object loses clarity and definition and must be sought for all over again.

If we consider our world platform as stable, then we are not viewing our distant goal with clarity and definition, since we do not yet even know what it is. We seldom know what our personal goal might be, much less the goal of the complex of mankind.

A tree is one of the most stable organisms in nature, and one of the most remarkable. Without a pumping mechanism it can draw fluid-nourishment hundreds of feet skyward toward its crown. In a way, it is a uniped: going nowhere yet casting its seed upon the wind; converting animal-waste into animal-necessity in a process of photosynthesis which uses carbon dioxide and expels oxygen. And while a tree draws almost half of its fluid nourishment from the surrounding air, more than half its sustenance comes from roots sunk deeply or widely into the earth.

So it is with the human observer, who can achieve stability only by joining past to present. When this becomes difficult or unpalatable man becomes rootless, buffeted by gusts from the East or the West. If our mushrooming present so blinds us that our past is lost in shadow, then we are now truly rootless, and all our haste will not ease our escape or lend meaning to our travels.

If an equation were attempted to measure the rate of mankind's progress, it would become self-evident that the rate of progress constantly accelerates. For example: if it took X years for the human organism to discover the wheel, it took considerably less than that, perhaps one thousand or five thousand years, for the next major emergence. From the steam locomotive to the automobile consumed a certain number of years. From the automobile to the aircraft the time consumed was considerably shortened. From propeller-driven aircraft to jet-propelled aircraft even less time was needed; and from jet-propelled aircraft to missiles, still less time. From terrestrial missiles to space missiles only a minute fraction of time was consumed.

The rate of progress constantly accelerates, which means that the rate of change constantly accelerates. This rapid rate has now brought us to the point where we live in a society of extraordinarily rapid modification. No sooner does one alteration emerge and present itself for evaluation than it is almost instantly made obsolete by another emergence clamoring for attention. How can we evaluate any of the emergences of our time when they are all relegated to the shadowed past more rapidly than the blinking of an eye?

When we say we have no time — no time for contemplation or identification of our own bearings — it is precisely because of our accelerated rate of change. Similar proddings relative to the rate of acceleration apply in great measure to nations, populations, and to all aspects of human endeavor.

Many ancient nations exerted power and influence for centuries. It is perhaps difficult to grasp the actuality that our country — the wealthiest of nations — was formed by a union of isolated colonies less than two hundred years ago, and that today we present promise and threat to the entire world. The U.S.S.R. was formed less than fifty years ago, and today, it too presents promise and threat to the entire world. Red China was formed fifteen years ago — and how soon will it present promise and threat to the entire world? And if South America, or Africa, were each to unite to found their own nations, how much time would elapse before they too presented promise and threat?

The basic reason for the accelerated rate of progress is man's ability — unique in all of nature — to transmit patterns of acquired knowledge and values to succeeding generations. This transmission has steadily resulted in increased specialization to the point where even mankind's strivings are compartmentalized and labeled like the canned foods that are disgorged with such mechanized regularity, often with more effort and money spent on the glistening attention-arresting labels than on the contents of the can.

Such a society of course rejects as a faulty product the individual who refuses to be compartmentalized, and who attempts to fulfill his life as a total human being. This assembly line was not designed for such a man; and the electronic eye, protector of uniformity, casts him aside.

Since our society still has too many such uncompartmentalized rejects, the motivational and behavorial research technicians are called upon, not to redesign the assembly line, but to try to redesign the rejected man.

In livestock-feeding experiments and practice, a herd of two-year-old steers — perhaps a hundred of them — are brought into a suitable feeding pen. Within a few days the livestockman will readily identify those of his animals that are aggressive feeders and those that are timid feeders. Since aggressive feeders normally add more to their body weight than timid feeders, this differentiation has economic importance to the livestockmen. The aggressive feeders are then quarantined in a separate pen; the timid feeders are similarly quarantined, and the majority of the animals, normal feeders, are left alone.

Inevitably, here is what happens. Among the timid feeders, some animals soon become aggressive, some remain timid, and the others become average feeders. A similar stratification occurs among the previously normal feeders. In the aggressive pen, many remain aggressive, many become timid, and relatively few become so-called normal feeders. If the same separation occurs once again, similar results are obtained. If too many separations are attempted, the entire feeding experiment collapses due to feeding neuroses.

The livestockman cannot make all his animals aggressive or timid; neither can he consistently quarantine the aggressive ones; he can scarcely identify them except as they are related, in the same pen, with the timid ones.

While motivational and behaviorial technicians assume a herd-resemblance in man, man is not a steer to be fattened for the market place.

Are we then so penned, so compartmentalized, that we cannot escape, but must submit to being moved from one feeding pen to another until we are ready for slaughter?

Of course not.

If the separate governments of a segmented Earth have mounted the world platform, and we have become a captive audience, then the question is truly this: What can the performers offer us so that we pay our entrance fee willingly — a fee that is not returnable? If all they can offer is promise coupled to threat, then the fee was much too high and their value as performers is overrated.

What can the individual do to retain his sanity in a world that is, clearly, not sane? Is man then doomed by the rate of his acceleration, which gives him no peace?

Of course not.

Man, the wildest and most untamable animal in all of nature, is never doomed as long as he rejects timidity and self-indulgence. It is certainly time he began to cherish his untamability as his greatest personal asset in a world being made increasingly chaotic by the erratic contortions of platform performers who have such obvious contempt for their audience.

Man is never doomed; but his mechanical extensions can be.

(November 24, 1961)

XVI

Garbage Disposal — A Nuclear Dilemma

LET US ACCEPT a massive assumption. Not that a superior astral aggressor is threatening Earth, and that East and West have united to repel an invader who considers man an edible delicacy. Let us assume that the threat of war has been eliminated and that peace is more or less respectable for, let us say, fifty years. Population, water, and food problems have been fairly well solved; and the people of the world have been released from animal-toil through nuclear power.

What do we do with our garbage, both common and nuclear?

In 1940 the people of the United States accumulated an average of two pounds of garbage per person per day, for a national total of some 50 million tons a year. Twenty years later, in 1960, the garbage averaged a little more than 3.5 lbs per person per day, for a national total of some 115 million tons a year. New York City alone generates an annual volume of garbage sufficient to fill a freight train spanning more than a continent, reaching from Manhattan to Seattle and on to San Francisco.

All this, you realize, is common garbage — not nuclear waste.

While the population of our country between 1940 and 1960 increased by some 33 percent, the garbage pile increased by some 130 percent. This increase is a direct result of enticing technical advances. Foods and drinks come in all sorts of disposable packages; and almost everything purchasable today — from an electric bulb to a child's toy — lasts a much shorter time than it used to and must be garbaged sooner.

The disposal of even common garbage presents an increasingly serious problem. Open dumping is frowned upon because it promotes all sorts of infestations and endangers the health of neighboring communities. Sanitary land-fill is becoming difficult because available land for this purpose is becoming increasingly scarce. Burning is discouraged because of air-pollution; river and lake disposal is discouraged because of water-pollution. Home garbage-disposal units are unsatisfactory because of the excessive water needed in their operation and because of their water-polluting factors. Ocean dumping harms marine life, dirties beaches, and is, of course, of little interest to inland cities. Composting garbage into fertilizer, while feasible to a degree, is expensive and could upset the economy of the fertilizer industry.

A serious project has been contemplated for compressing garbage and then hurling it into space. Upon re-entering the Earth's atmosphere, it would burn up into dust, and disperse upon the planet some of the resources previously removed. Radioactive garbage, of course, presents other and totally different problems.

The growth of nuclear power in the United States, for non-war or peaceful purposes, has been estimated by numerous authorities in the field. The National Academy of Sciences agrees that by 1980 the principal source of fission products will be from power-reactor operations. In 1960 the Academy reported:

> In a future nuclear economy, the volumes of power reactor wastes to be handled must be considered in relation to the cumulative quantity of radioactivity being generated by other atomic energy operations. At the present time, the waste volumes and activities from stationary power reactors obviously are small when compared with those of government production and test reactors. It appears reasonable to expect that by 1965 there will be in the range of 10,000 to 20,000 thermal megawatts of power-reactor capacity in the U.S.A.; and that by 1980 this figure will grow to about 100,000 thermal megawatts or more. The total fission product inventory resulting from the processing of spent power-reactor fuels in 1980 has been estimated at 10 billion curies. About 800 million curies will be strontium-90 . . .

One curie is, of course, a huge amount of radioactivity. For comparison purposes, radioactivity in air is usually measured in micro-micro-curies per cubic metre of air. A micro-micro-curie is a millionth of a millionth of a curie — a small but accurately measurable quantity. To present some idea of what 800 million curies of spent power-reactor fuels represent — if this material were spread over every acre of the continental U.S.A. and were contained within one metre above the land, the radioactivity readings for every acre of our country would be some 4,000,000 micro-micro-curies of strontium 90 for that one cubic metre throughout the land. Again, for comparison purposes only, cities in the U.S.A.

presently average considerably less than 10 micro-micro-curies of radioactivity per cubic metre of air.

All this is a mathematical explanation with no relationship to reality; it merely depicts the magnitude of the disposal problem of radioactive garbage resulting from even peaceful uses of atomic energy. And nobody yet knows what to do about it.

People seem to be especially troubled about strontium-90. Of course, many other radioactive substances emerge from atomic energy besides strontium-90. This particular substance is the one most frequently mentioned because its unique combination of qualities makes it especially dangerous. It is one of the more abundant products of nuclear fission. Its half-life (that period during which potency is reduced by 50 percent) of 27 years is long enough to keep it active, yet short enough to make it a strong radiator, since usually the shorter the half-life, the stronger the radiation of any substance. Chemically, strontium-90 is very similar to calcium, and so is taken up and concentrated by bone tissue. The rate of calcium utilization is greater in the growing young organism than in the physically mature, hence the young have a greater uptake of strontium-90, which is known to cause bone cancer in experimental animals. In a nuclear explosion, much of strontium-90 does not fall back to the ground within a short time and within a short distance of the point of the explosion; instead, it is spread gradually over the entire Earth. The winds of the lower part of the atmosphere carry tropospheric fallout around the world in latitudes fairly close to the latitude of detonation. Russia's detonations, usually in the Arctic, carry tropospheric fallout around the northern latitudes; America's detonations, usually near the Equator, carry tropospheric fallout around equatorial latitudes of Central America and southern Asia. The winds of the upper part of the atmosphere carry stratospheric fallout. Stratospheric fallout results when larger explosions are detonated higher in the atmosphere. Regardless of where the detonations are exploded — in arctic or equatorial regions — the physical condition of stratospheric winds in their normal polar drifts are such that the particles they carry spread over the entire Earth, and may take years before their normal drifts bring them back to the Earth, usually in springtime rainfall. Most radioactive substances contained in the original debris generated and hurled aloft by nuclear explosions burn themselves out by the time they return to Earth. But strontium-90 may take two, three, or more years before some 75 percent of the original strontium-90 of a particular blast returns to Earth. However all sorts of other radioactive substances resulting from atomic energy uses are not placed in the atmosphere, where partial dilution could result.

The problems of radioactive garbage disposal — even from peaceful uses of nuclear energy — are infinitely complex; and nobody yet knows what to do about them. While research continues in this area, the effort expended is not only minor compared to that expended for the nuclear projects that are the garbage generators, but the effort is also regional and segmented.

Even the term "radioactive waste" is not at all descriptive of the nature of the problem, which also consists of the concentration of radioactive material, the total quantity of radioactivity in the garbage, the isotopic composition of the waste, and its chemical and physical nature. These complex variables must also be considered in terms of their environment, which they constantly modify.

One of the three major factors to be considered in nuclear garbage disposal is the maximum quantity of various radioactive isotopes allowable in the human body — especially in terms of genetic effects on future generations. Of this factor we know shockingly little. We know that all radiation is genetically harmful; any radiation dose however small, whether natural or man-made, can induce some mutations at some point. And almost all mutations are harmful to succeeding generations as each generation increases its number of what has been called the "slight detrimentals." Nature eventually removes these from the hereditary pool through premature death or through their inability to produce a normal number of normal offspring. All peoples of the world have always carried a supply of spontaneous mutant-genes resulting from natural causes; and nearly all of these spontaneous mutant-genes are harmful. Any additional radiation above the natural background produces mutations in addition to the spontaneous ones. The size of the supply of mutant-genes represents a balance between the tendency of old mutants to eliminate themselves and the tendency of new ones to appear.

It is this delicate balance that man-made radiation tends to upset. It should be made quite clear that what matters in this context is the total dose of radiation received by an individual throughout his entire productive lifetime. Because genetic damage done by radiation is cumulative, all radiation is harmful. At this point, the hereditary pool of man throughout the ages has, perhaps, not yet been damaged beyond recall. However, there is a point — a proper theoretical point — at which genetic damage resulting from radiation to man's hereditary pool will extinguish the species. This point of inevitable no-return, while theoretical, can become actual; and nobody knows how close or how distant we are.

Nobody knows.

Monumental exertions in basic research are needed here, yet very little is being done because of a shortage of scientists in this area; and especially because current radiation data quickly becomes masked prior to evaluation. This masking is a result of the constantly varying radiation conditions brought about by continued atomic energy work throughout the world, which makes impossible the establishment of a stable base of reference.

Despite the fact that infinite harm to all remaining future generations can result from even the peaceful uses of atomic radiation, very little teaching of genetics is being carried on in the universities of the world. A wrathful Jehovah once threatened to visit the sins of the father upon the children unto the third or fourth generation; now, the sins can be visited unto whatever generations remain.

This is not meant as a briefing on genetics, however, but as a comment on some of the problems of nuclear garbage disposal.

The second factor in nuclear garbage disposal is the specific nature of the radioactive waste resulting from a specific operation. This is a highly variable factor with each operation, and general findings are of little value. An operations manual for nuclear garbage disposal would, at this point, have little application.

The third factor is the physical, chemical, and biological characteristics of the environment into which the garbage is to be released. We know appallingly little about this factor, which is so intimately inter-related with our environment on, above, and below ground (the movements of winds and ocean currents that, of course, are not governed by man-made boundaries). In this regard, considering garbage disposal from even the peaceful uses of atomic energy, our planet is certainly one world and any attempt at its fragmentation is scientifically absurd. For us to accumulate any sort of useful knowledge regarding this disposal factor, worldwide cooperation is a basic requirement.

The combined behavior of these three factors of nuclear garbage disposal presents another series of problems that are, of themselves, infinitely complex.

An indication of this complexity is to consider what may happen if radioactive garbage were dumped into the sea, even in small quantities, and even if gigantic egg beaters were used to blend and dilute the radioactive wastes with all the waters of all the oceans and seas. All marine life would promptly begin re-constituting and re-concentrating the radioactive wastes; shellfish would do a highly efficient job with strontium-90; and all fish would take on radioactive iodine, zinc, cesium, and numerous other substances. Fish process millions upon millions of gallons of water in order to secure their oxygen and food requirements. Larger fish feed on smaller fish, and thereby process many times the millions upon millions of gallons of water of their prey. Chemical and sea-water reclamation projects would also re-concentrate the radioactive wastes.

Here again, basic research obviously can be only an international cooperative effort. While such basic research continues in this area, the effort expended is infinitesimal when compared with expenditures for those nuclear devices that are the generators of the garbage.

That man should continue to add to nuclear wastes at this point in his ignorance is monumentally stupid.

We have not yet evaluated the data thus far gathered; and further nuclear testing hampers basic research by masking with overlays of man-made radiation those findings we must secure in order to leash this uncomfortable beast before ever we attempt to tame him.

Nobody seems to know what he is doing, even in terms of garbage disposal.

We can, however, attempt to find out.

From a scientific aspect, all nuclear energy power manipulations all over the world should stop, and atomic energy projects should be returned to the basic scientists for further evaluation in terms of their ecology and of their inter-relationship with their total environment.

Among the cruel deceptions enveloping Man on Earth, none is more brutal than the contemporary concepts involving the peaceful uses of atomic energy.

At present there are no harmless peaceful uses of atomic radiation except as a meticulously controlled tool for further basic atomic research, very little of which is currently being pursued anywhere in the world. The authority for this statement is the National Academy of Sciences, established during our Civil War in 1863 under a Congressional Charter signed by Abraham Lincoln; and its much broader National Research Council, established by the Academy during the First World War in 1916 at the request of Woodrow Wilson.

Despite the citing of authorities and the detailing of horror, is it possible for man truly to grasp the significance of his dilemma in his chaotic and almost irreversible thrust toward extinction? Can he truly comprehend the theoretical concept of his own ending in a world where words have lost their meaning and facts their impact, and where people seem to be stirred only by gross emotions of fear and greed and hate? This loss of the meaning of words and the impact of facts is, in itself, a clear indication that man has also lost all sense of his own value and position. Little wonder then that he can be so easily subjected to mass delusion manipulated either from the East or the West.

As we hurtle on in our stampede of confusion, nowhere is even once voice that commands universal respect raised to identify our bearings. Only a few years ago we had many voices universally respected in physics, mathematics, chemistry, and biology, whose statements were trusted by all mankind. Now, our times seem to defy leadership even in an area as seemingly universal as two-plus-two-equals-four.

It is true that today occasional groups of individual scientists sign public letters urging sanity, which is, of course, in short supply; but having published their urgencies they return to their universities, agencies, and laboratories to continue their work for the same leaders whose minds they have, apparently, attempted to sway. One never hears of these same scientists rejecting contract-research, the purpose of which, more often than not, is total destruction. It is impossible to take their protests seriously.

Late in 1961 we were confronted by a Nobel Laureate's popular nationally syndicated articles on how to build a fallout shelter for thirty dollars. Not so well publicized was the fact that the laureate's own shelter — built according to his economical plan — burned to ashes during the fires that destroyed many multi-hundred-thousand-dollar homes of film notables. Of course, it was explained, the thirty-dollar shelter was designed only for a gentle zephyr of fallout — not for a holocaust.

In one of its 1960 reports on the effects of atomic radiation, the Academy of Sciences stated that the general public may

> . . . well be left with a feeling of dismay because of the apparent lack of unanimity of opinion among those to whom it wishes to turn as experts. The difficulty confronting the scientist is that many of the essential facts necessary to arrive at the answers sought are not yet available, and — what is worse — are unlikely to be quickly available, despite the scientist's best efforts. Because he is under great pressure for an answer, the scientist is forced uneasily into extrapolation or prediction. It is here that the grey areas of apparent disagreement develop . . .

This is unquestionably true, and unquestionably not the whole truth. Many scientists extrapolate or predict willingly and even anxiously; this is especially true when they seek further public funds for their pet projects. Instead of being scrubbed by public contempt, they are piously sprinkled with public acclaim.

Many scientists publicly announce that properly constructed fallout shelters can offer protection to their inmates in the event of a defensive nuclear or thermonuclear war, while many of their colleagues maintain — equally publicly — that fallout shelters can offer no protection against thermonuclear warfare, either offensive or defensive. Still others, seeking some compromise — no matter how uncomfortable — believe that, while properly constructed fallout shelters may offer some protection, the price for this protection is much too high in terms of the effects of national brutalization and the consequences of the use of thermonuclear warfare as an instrument of international policy.

Most of the scientists who hold any of these opinions are honorable men. But whom does one trust? Certainly the majority of scientists in both East and West — even those struggling so mightily and so dishearteningly to accelerate Red China's nuclear weaponry potential — are competent, honorable men. Yet — whom does one trust?

It would seem that trust, like peace, has become part of the race memory of the species. It is presently absent, but hopefully recallable.

Our clever devices have brought us to that point in space and time where progress can only be defined as equal fear equally shared. Personal aspirations no longer possess inherent value, but must be evaluated only as part of a strategy for the conquest of an enemy. Must we constantly measure ourselves against an enemy? On this so rapidly shrinking and fear-sprayed planet, is man's highest achievement the conquest of his neighbor — and, through this conquest, his own accelerated destruction?

The instinct toward war may or may not be an inerasable part of man's nature; the instinct toward self-extermination clearly is not. Thermonuclear warfare is today neither offensive nor defensive, but mutually destructive. By comparison with an all-out bacteriological, chemical, and thermonuclear world conflict, the Second World War had all the gentleness of knights jousting at King Arthur's Court.

There was a time when a scientist cherished his integrity; now he cherishes his security. Contemporary science is a cosmic mockery of its potentialities.

The fallout-shelter hysteria and delusion brutalizing America through surges of fear, diluting our defense against the wrong enemy, is only one of the manifestations of scientific deception involving nuclear energy — a deception that is enveloping the entire world in a hot haze through which clear vision is impossible. It would seem that East and West, possessing more similarities than differences, have a real and common enemy — man's ignorance of and stupidity toward himself and his ecology. Yet the two Titans remain locked stupidly in mortal combat while the rising waters embrace them both.

This is not meant to be pessimistic. Pessimism is the doctrine that reality is essentially evil, that the evils of life overbalance the happiness it affords. Pessimism is an inclination to put the least favorable construction upon actions and happenings. It is, in fact, defeat. But man is not defeated so long as he strives to retain his individuality, to broaden and deepen his objectivity, to establish for himself a personal morality.

When the Bomb exploded on Hiroshima, the world, as it then existed, was shattered; national boundaries and historic concepts of national sovereignties became extinct, and a man-induced genetic mutation took place throughout all the members of the family of nations. We are cumulatively and irreversibly reconstituted into one world or none. Our planet is now fused. This would be true if no other bomb had ever again been exploded in peace or war.

Is the insane concept — that we are now involved in a *war* for *peace* — one of the manifestations of our mutation?

Who are the wounded in this war for peace?

Actually — who are not?

(November 17, 1961)

XVII

Scientific Realism and Humanism

MAN HAD A beginning on Earth. Whatever frame of reference is used for his emergence — whether stemming from theology, philosophy, or science — he had a beginning; and, therefore, he will also have an ending. Probably neither beginning nor ending can be grasped by the human mind, which cannot conceive eternity nor contain infinity. Even in mathematics, which has a useful symbol for infinity, the concept itself is not a stimulus for further contemplation or infinite exploration. Concept and symbol of infinity are actually limiting factors indicating that the mathematical formulations have been extended as far as necessary for proof, disproof, or conjecture, and further extensions are either repetitious or meaningless. The symbol and concept of infinity are useful precisely because they are restrictive.

It is a mathematical certainty that man's time on Earth is limited; whether he is closer to his beginning or to his ending is quite meaningless. The meaning is in our being here, and in the fact that each of us, as an individual, is the sole container of a personal eternity, of whatever infinity each of us can grasp. As in mathematics, the concept of eternity can have meaning only if it is restrictive; only if we contain it with measurability and accept its responsibility.

Each of us had a beginning and each of us will have an ending. Does the fact of inevitable death continually modify life? The manner of death may do so, but not the fact of death — for who can live his life as though each breath were his last? Yet every day a little of us is reborn, and a little more of us dies. Between his own beginning and ending — a span simultaneously infinitesimal and personally eternal — the individual can achieve heights almost beyond imagining; but only, it would seem, if he accepts personal responsibility for his actions and his aims. If he does not accept continuing personal responsibility, or gives part of himself away to the safe-keeping of others, he amputates part of himself. If he does not accept his own individuality he ceases to be an individual and is no longer his own container of personal eternity. If he relinquishes his responsibility, he relinquishes his freedom. He can be free only if he retains responsibility; only if he can answer for his own conduct and obligations.

However, opportunities for the individual to think for himself seem to decrease with scientific and technical progress which, during this time of transition, adds to confusion far more than it generates clarity. Opportunities for the individual to effect change and to retain responsibility, even in his personal life, also diminish with scientific and technical progress. The constant additions being made to the application of scientific law prod society and the individual increasingly toward anarchy — that state of disorder and confusion where there is no law.

All of this is, of course, contradictory; and is probably a major source of individual and world torsion, of stress and strain and disharmony. The progress in which we are presently enmeshed should expand our personal horizons and lend dimension to our aspirations. Instead, it contracts the individual into a misshapen mass, which is then placed on a cunningly contrived pedestal as a work of modern technologic art. Thus elevated, we soon find ourselves seduced by all the skills of the communications aspects of politics, business, cultural, and behavioral sciences not only into paying admission to see ourselves but into admiring our own distortion — even while we remain captive on our own treadmill.

Scientific and technical progress so often seems to be directed only toward making the treadmill revolve more smoothly and rapidly in all aspects of daily living, forcing the individual to deplete himself even while he moves faster and faster toward his exhaustion and immobility. For the individual to effect change, to remove himself from the accelerating treadmill, requires courage and increasing skill, a skill he cannot easily develop so long as his energies are mainly directed at keeping his footing on the treadmill. Soon — and all too readily — he relinquishes his responsibility toward himself, and with his responsibility, his freedom. Responsibility presupposes awareness. But how can the individual expand his awareness, and with awareness, his responsibility and thereby his freedom, so long as he remains captive on his treadmill while cleverly designed montages slide by to give him a false sense of progress?

Can the individual risk getting off his treadmill? Or, more to the point: Can he risk remaining on it?

Without question, the scientific-technologic community throughout the world continues to make measurable contributions toward easing the life of mankind in medicine, agriculture, chemistry, transportation, communication — in almost all fields of human endeavor that can be measured materially. This is one side of a scale. Benefits of science and technology must be paid for — this is the other side of the scale, where the price the individual pays is the relinquishment of his individuality and his descent into the mass, there to become diluted even beyond self-recognition. This price seems to be unavoidable and many are quite happy to pay it. While there is a growing awareness that the balance is askew, what can the individual do about it for himself? Certainly he is not without personal guilt and responsibility in his harvest of confusion.

In spite of being deluged by an explosion of information as massive as the population-explosion of our age, we seem to be confused regarding simple meaning and purpose. We have allowed ourselves to be lured into thinking that the bigness of our data-pile demonstrates the greatness of our lives. Even in our search for a personal identity — a search pursued by so many with such shattering experiences — so few of us exert ourselves to seek answers for ourselves; rather, we readily accept those answers that are neatly packaged by adept hucksters.

This is part of the continuing price we pay for the dehumanizing process in our search — not for simplicities but for ease.

The mechanical ease of acquisition of material things — the stated goal of nations and peoples throughout the world — affects even our striving toward non-material concepts and principles. Each of us can see manifestations of this in our own environments, on all sorts of levels and with varying degrees of intensity. Ease of acquisition, whether of pretested objects or of safe ideas, usually dulls our desire for, use, and comprehension of, our acquisitions. Knowledge or grandeur and clarity of emotion, demanding major personal exertion for possession, usually remain unsought for and unpossessed. So many other availabilities can be acquired so much more readily.

An acquisition is that which is purchasable for a price and is readily replaceable through various degrees of exertion. A possession is that to which the individual contributes something of himself; it is neither readily purchasable nor replaceable. This distinction between acquisition and possession is especially valid for human emotion in its various manifestations: love, freedom, dignity, morality, and a continuing realization of personal value.

In every mechanized society, whether family or nation, acquisitions quite readily displace possessions; and when this happens society becomes increasingly shallow toward values and their appreciation.

Certainly it is easier today to acquire books, for example, than to possess their contents; to acquire information than to possess knowledge; to acquire an education than to possess wisdom. Technical publications are available by the ton, but their comprehension can be measured by the milligram. So many of the scientific community hasten their bits and pieces into print mainly from fear of being beaten to the page by their even more hasty colleagues; and so many of them publish the same articles and notes year after year, sending them on from publication to publication, where they add to the clutter. When some of these articles reach newspapers, pre-digested magazines, and commentators, the public is sprayed with gasp-inducing inanities.

Even in fiction, that remarkable indicator of a society's strivings and comprehension, where we once had the concepts of *War and Peace*, *Crime and Punishment*, today we have *Franny and Zooey*.

During any 24-hour period in our country, probably more people hear Beethoven through radio and recordings than listened to him during his entire lifetime; yet how many listen, and how many use him merely as background music while dividing their attention among a half-dozen other activities, each clamoring for a shallow segment of response?

Even the American family-unit, beneficiary of mechanical acquisitions beyond the widest grasp of story-kings, seems to possess decreasing depth and unity. Accepting shallowness and its accompanying stickiness as his way of life, wondering as he wanders through his years, what does the individual member of this unit say for himself about morality or ethics or humanism? Nobody really forces him to accept shallowness; he does it for himself, leading his family behind him. Busy with his acquisitions, the individual is seldom aware that those who profess to speak for him so frequently regard him with a kind of pious contempt.

If this is the sort of acquiescent existence he wants, the technologic community is more than ready to oblige him. And soon — all too soon — he becomes inured to all sorts of dilemmas, accepting dilemma itself as a way of life.

This, too, is a treadmill which can exhaust the individual into forgetfulness and immobility.

Perhaps forgetting is more important to individual survival than remembering, for who among us could survive if he must constantly remember all past agony and despair? And yet, for the individual not to remember constantly that the ultimate achievement of scientific application, thus far, is mutual and terminal threat, would be to embrace suicide as a way of life and death as a personal passion.

Probably the two great parent-materials of our time are scientific realism and humanism. It is the contention here that each, by itself, holds little promise for the survival of mankind; however, their genetic compounding may present a philosophic concept for our age permitting the individual to seek his own identity and purpose, his individual place in nature as his right because of the fact of life; a concept to help fulfill his realization of being no less than the universe-in-miniature.

Scientific realism describes those universal apolitical concepts that do not depend upon acceptance or rejection by political ideologies, and that do not lend themselves to emotional exploitation since they are of themselves universal, applying with equal vigor and measure to each of us. All of basic science is in this category; much of applied technology is not, mainly because it is essentially regional in conception, execution, and exploitation.

Humanism describes the concept that man is more than simply the highest animal on Earth, and more than a series of equations or a pawn in international, and often lethal, conflicts; a concept that reaches far beyond the early Twentieth Century dichotomies of Socialism and Capitalism, which are labels describing the past — hardly the present, and certainly not the future.

Neither scientific realism nor humanism, by themselves, permit man any sort of fulfillment of his potentialities. Through its applicators and administrators, and despite its vast contributions in many fields, science has brought mankind to the theoretical possibility of total extinction. If left to itself, science, increasingly becoming a group-activity, becomes parthenogenetic, birthing replicas of itself, and continually increasing its contributions even while compounding its threat. In order to function, humanism, which is essentially an individual expression, would have to disregard this ultimate threat from science as though it did not exist — which is unrealistic and impossible.

The individual, despite or because of all the manifestations of technical progress, finds it increasingly difficult to function as an individual. So many of these manifestations offer such enormous benefit to the individual, he finds it nearly impossible to reject them. And why should he?

Actually, even if he wanted to, they are impossible to avoid. It would seem that the individual must descend, even if rebelliously, into some acquiescent uniformity for his own survival. The point here is that uniformity and immobility are intimately related; and that uniformity results in immobility, while immobility of the individual cannot be secured without uniformity. Technical progress cannot expand without uniformity. Throughout the world people strive for the benefits of technical progress; they seem to be quite willing to pay for it by accepting uniformity, which will inevitably prod them into immobility.

How can the individual benefit from progress without succumbing to it, without losing his individuality, while retaining whatever ability he possesses to think for himself, in the direction of his own life? This is a pivotal question that can be asked in many ways: Can the individual liberate himself from historic pieties, moral absolutisms, fear of and hope from the supernatural? Can he emerge from the morass of self-created fears? In other words, can he survive and find meaning in his own survival and purpose in his own life?

Because of the contradictory nature of life today as exposed and unanswered by science, perhaps because unanswerable by science alone, these questions now seem to be more vital than ever before in man's history.

The historic pieties and moral absolutisms no longer seem valid in a world confronting mutual and terminal manmade threat, in a world where man can assure his own extinction but not his own continuance. Fear of, and hope from, the supernatural have long been exposed as stemming from mankind's primitiveness and avarice.

Emergence from the morass of self-created fears can be achieved essentially through individual knowledge and acceptance of individual responsibility for actions and aims, without dependence upon a non-existent higher absolution.

All this is hugely difficult because the individual places inner restraints upon himself and demands of himself great expenditures to possess and maintain standards of personal morality and ethics rather than the so-easily acquired herd-morality and herd-ethics. Great effort is needed for the individual to accumulate knowledge to judge for himself and to evaluate his own inter-relationship with his total environment. Great strength and courage are needed to reject gibberish, no matter how seemingly well-documented, and to be guided by principle emerging out of personal awareness instead of by expediency, which is action conducive to special advantage rather than to the more broadly beneficial. This approach to life has come to be known as humanism.

Surrounded by uniformity and immobility, humanism is not acquired easily or retained effortlessly; yet nothing less than humanism permits the individual to retain any sort of personal dignity or sense of personal value. Humanism is a liberating concept, permitting the individual to cast off the shackles of historic pieties and moral absolutisms, of dependence upon the supernatural for praise or punishment. Humanism can set dimensions for the individual so that he can identify his self-created fears and expose them to the light of reason. Precisely because it is an individual concept, humanism is not restricted by geographic segments, or by externally imposed ritual, or by externally imposed allegiances. It is truly an apolitical concept involving all of mankind; but it is not license, not freedom abused. The individual who becomes less insular because of broader awareness of the world does not reject his immediate environment. Often, if the individual achieves broader perspective from his physical and intellectual travels, the result is quite the contrary; his immediate environment assumes greater value since he can extract more from it and offer more to it, precisely because he has broadened and deepened his frame of reference to himself.

This, it would seem, is the essence of loyalty.

But even here, how effective is humanism when confronted by the non-humanist scientific realities that do not depend upon individual acceptance or rejection for their existence and impact? Regardless of his beliefs, the person who is cut bleeds. How effective, then, is humanism?

Perhaps not very effective at all. While other philosophies can and do offer some moral basis for man's inhumanity and irresponsibility, humanism does not offer the individual any sort of moral ease or absolution or irresponsibility.

Man's inhumanity is not a manifestation of the Wrath of God, but of individual irresponsibility. The repetition of man's inhumanity throughout history does not make it divine, since history itself has no divine attributes or historic rights. Historic rights are meaningless because this moment, too, is history. Man's inhumanity does not stem from his inevitable cosmic loneliness and despair since these are not his fundamental emotions from which he cannot escape, to which he is tied by the fact of his existence. The individual can feel whatever emotion he truly possesses through personal awareness and personal responsibility. Emotions that are merely acquired through enticement by skillful manipulators are not sufficiently stable for the extraction of the individual's bearings and direction. This is so because a possession — whether material or emotional — is that to which the individual has contributed something of himself; while an acquisition — whether material or spuriously emotional — can so readily be replaced by more skillful enticement.

Man's glory, equally, is not a manifestation of the Joy of God, or the breaching of cosmic despair, or Historic Correctness which seems to have assumed for itself some sort of divinity. Man's glory, it would seem, is his totality, achieved only through personal awareness and responsibility.

In this context, it is the individual who can possess the strength of unity, while any divinity can be only the sum of mankind itself.

It would seem that science, by expanding mankind's horizons even as it expands the threat of mankind's actual existence, has, as its basic contribution, brought man a realization of his own capacity, of his own potentiality. Mutual and terminal threat is fact and cannot be ignored; it was generated from the quicksand of individual irresponsibility. Anarchy stemming from the expedient applications of science and scientific law is directly attributable to individual irresponsibility of scientists and officials of government, regardless of political persuasion — directly attributable to individuals who maintain the government–science–industry complexes throughout the world. These complexes can exist precisely because, within them, individual responsibility does not exist.

If science cannot be modified by humanism, the brilliance of the nuclear flash can continue to scar man's clarity and dim his awareness of his environment, including himself.

Certainly one of man's greatest achievements toward humanism, toward the recognition and appreciation of the individual as a whole human being, has been the concept of monotheism, of an eternal God before whom one could lay down his burdens at the end of the day and the end of his many days; a God of continuity and justice; of enveloping warmth and understanding; of infinite wisdom and love.

The individual gods of primitive peoples and their primitive pantheisms had geographic boundaries which set limits to their conquests and strivings. At such boundaries, where cultures merged, the gods fought for supremacy and for the

allegiance of the subject-peoples, who so often rejected them
if they could be defeated. These gods were tangible; they
were personal, intimate, and limited gods, demanding tangible sacrifice. They were not at all expressions of humanism
or sanctity of life.

When humanism emerged, with its intangibility and universality, man's bestiality toward man was never more rampant than in the name of this same emerging humanism. The
various Crusades of the Dark Ages — the Holy Wars of the
Saracens against the Infidels; the Holy Inquisition by the
self-anointed against those they labelled "unbelievers";
the conquest of continents and enslavement of proud cultures
— were all in the name of this humanism. Many thousands
were sacrificed in its name. Yet these early Believers were
not essentially evil men. The more this humanism spread,
the more refined did its skills emerge in uncovering those to
be sacrificed; and' when overt greed thrust all semblance of
humanism aside — as it did in the conquest of South America,
for example — the pennant of humanism, a mask behind
which lurked enslavement and decay, was flaunted brazenly.

The primitive gods functioned in a physically compartmentalized world. As knowledge of the world expanded and
living became more complex, this compartmentalization
undoubtedly generated awkward barriers which could be
breached through an expanding humanism and through a
concept of monotheism, of a universal God, father of all mankind, for whom no barriers could exist. It was a liberating
concept. Would the Israelites have followed Moses from
slavery to wander in the wilderness without his concept of
monotheism as a guide and promise of safe emergence? It is
doubtful that man's exploration and exploitation of his own
planet could have been pursued unless he had had more than
a passing faith in an eternal and universal guide and protector
from whom safety and just rewards would flow everlastingly.

It is doubtful that man could have reached his present state of science, his present dilemma of mutual and terminal threat, unless he had exploited, in his progress, his more than passing faith in a universal humanism, and in a monotheistic God of continuity and love.

This is the basic dilemma of our age; that scientific realism, and even humanism, by themselves, can assure man only of his total annihilation and, in the process, constrict him into tighter compartmentalization. This seems to be the cosmic mockery: that nations, striving monumentally toward a goal of self-indulgence, threaten to spatter mankind to oblivion or to exhaust mankind as a sacrifice in the name of love — love for man, for God, for power.

Perhaps love can be defined as a feeling of strong personal attachment induced by sympathetic understanding or by ardent affection. Yet love, in all its external and internal manifestations, is only a lens which can modify, sharpen, clarify, enlarge, or blur that which is seen through it — something must first be there to be seen. Love is a lens that can offer perspective to the viewer; seemingly it can bring the viewed object closer or move it farther away, and, in the process, soften or enlarge blemishes. And like a lens, if held steadfast long enough, assuming there is time, it can focus even cold late-afternoon winter sunlight into a point-of-warmth or into a point-of-fire that, when controlled, can banish later darkness or, when uncontrolled, can flare and consume the holder and his environment and even melt the lens itself.

All this and more love, as the finest of lenses, can accomplish — but only if something is there. It can so magnify time that time itself seems to stop, thereby offering a sense of eternity. But if nothing is present, the finest and greatest of lenses can modify only — nothing; and can so magnify the void until it is almost beyond the scope of man's understanding. Love is not a mirror that retains the image when the subject moves away from it. Neither is it a solvent that dissolves deep pessimism into a joy greater than optimism — since who would dig a trough at the foot of Mount Everest in order to make the climb higher and more rewarding?

Of course love is a great ecologic force, modifying the comprehension and appreciation of everything seen through it. It is an attribute only of man, only of the individual, in whom it is often noble. When it becomes enmassed, it is often corrupt in all its manifestations.

Love of country can be noble in the individual; yet the Nazis murdered millions for love of country. Love for knowledge is certainly noble; yet its applications can be so very destructive.

When love becomes an enforced attribute of mass-man, as in most religions of the world where love for God is demanded upon penalty of eternal damnation, love can asphixiate the individual who strives to retain his individuality. It ceases to be love, which cannot be forced, and degenerates into nothing more valid than a glutinous emotion.

Is it possible that man's highest achievement toward humanism — his concept of monotheism, of one universal God of eternal justice — is not that at all, but his first step along the path leading to loss of his individualism, to his own enmassment and degeneration? If this is even remotely so, the fault is with man's concept and with his exploitation of his concept. Perhaps a universal God of eternal justice is only a bottomless container into which man can cast all sorts of exploitations and indulgences, and from which he can extract, at will, an endless supply of absolution.

The fact is inescapable that the threat of mutual and terminal annihilation cannot be just, and cannot be a manifestation of a universal God of eternal justice. Justice, in this context, has no meaning for man. How can justice, which is morality and ethics, apply to universal threat? And love, sometimes defined as the benevolence attributed to God, or man's adoration of God, has even less meaning in this context. The fact of the mass-threat, of the universal threat, remains with us. How can this be attributed to a universal God? But it most assuredly can be attributed to man; to his corruption of humanism and his self-enslavement to concepts that are constrictive; to his forcing of the individual into the mass-mold in the name of a universal God; and to his rejection of the basic attribute of the individual: that he is a whole human being and his own container of eternity.

Humanism, by itself, is parthenogenetic, birthing replicas of itself which permit no variation and no individualization. A universal God is equally parthenogenetic, permitting no variation and no individualization. And while these may be noble concepts, in actuality they have become brittle, readily shattered under stress, spraying their devotees with tearing splinters.

Scientific realism is an equally noble concept; its actuality, however, can become an insane perversion to destroy the world.

Scientific realism can be defined as those universal apolitical and amoral concepts that do not depend upon acceptance or rejection by ideologies; and that do not, of their own accord, lend themselves to political or emotional exploitation since they are universal of themselves, applying with equal vigor and measure to all of mankind.

Scientific realism is the roundness of the Earth, or the existence of the Universe, or this moment. These do not depend upon man's acceptance or rejection. They are there for man's awareness and discovery, and for him to draw whatever conclusions he may attempt — or no conclusions.

As heretofore mentioned, man's search for knowledge is as basic as the biologic beat of his heart. From primitive man searching for natural caves in which to preserve and perpetuate himself, throughout history to contemporary man searching for a way to preserve himself in concrete caves or bunkers, this assertion is valid.

Search cannot be separated from living, not even when knowledge acquired through search is used for man's own destruction. The search remains inevitable unless man becomes totally enmassed and immobilized. At that point of Absolute Zero there is neither movement, nor search, nor life. However, what can emerge from man's life and search can be evil when applied. Our inevitable search has now presented us with an acquisition that can, theoretically, obliterate the search itself. The foundation of religions and philosophies, in their repeated attempts to find man's place in nature, has been this historic dilemma of good-versus-evil. In a sense this is also the dilemma within humanism and within scientific realism.

A new concept of humanism is so very essential since scientific realism is so very unavoidable. Scientific realism itself, of course, is neither good nor evil; however, the actualities that emerge from scientific realism can be one or the other, depending upon man's application and manipulation.

Despite its concept of an eternal protector, the failure of historic humanism to guide man through his present wanderings in the wilderness and to assure him safe emergence is probably one of the basic causes of the strains and stresses of our society as we continually rise and fall to the gravitational effects of massive threat. Man no longer feels at ease within himself; nor can he extract bitter comfort from lamentation to a God that has forsaken him, since he has forsaken himself.

It is not a question of optimism or pessimism, but of reality. Optimism is the doctrine that the good of life over-balances the pain and evil of life; it is the inclination to put the most favorable construction upon actions and happenings and to hope for the best possible outcome. Optimism is the doctrine that our world is the best possible world. In reality, our world with all its glories and despite its dangers is, for us, the only world. But man increasingly feels himself or-phaned from his world and imprisoned in Limbo, that place of confinement confronting oblivion.

He now seeks a new humanism in the behavioral sciences, where psychologists and psychiatrists, the new priests work-ing in the stressed areas of human inter-relationships, will so smooth his path that even if he wanders in the wilderness of his own making, he will be made blissfully unaware of any danger.

Psychologists and psychiatrists strive to tear down bar-riers within and among people so that the individual becomes smoothly adjusted and capable of sliding easily into his society, there to find his comfort and his destiny.

Actually, should such barriers be torn down? Should energies be expended in their elimination in order that life be made an undifferentiated plane? Perhaps so. But perhaps bridges could be constructed over these barriers by using the barriers themselves as bridge-supports or observation-towers from which to view from some perspective; thereby also eliminating the scavenger-need to remove the debris of torn-down barriers.

Barriers, when recognized and evaluated, can often serve as markers against which one can measure himself. When everything becomes the same, how does an individual recog-nize himself?

In the attempt at an emerging humanism, cause-and-effect inter-relationships are supreme, and behavior is re-stricted to attempts at controlling effects by the manipulation of causes. For example, if the child cries because he is hungry, then feed him and stop his crying. Cause-and-effect: manipulate the cause, and the effect is controlled. And while it is seldom so simple an inter-relationship or so clear-cut a manipulation, the behavioral sciences today are being hoisted as promise of safe emergence from our wilderness.

But who will manipulate the manipulators and who will extract meaning from their findings? Here again, in the hypnotic and narcotic promise of manipulators — who, in order to succeed, must divest the individual of his individuality and seek to achieve precisely those self-considered accomplishments of historic humanism — we seek ease rather than substance, and acquisition rather than possession.

However, if humanism can modify science as a prism separates brilliant sunlight into a measurable spectrum, man's fabled glory on Earth can perhaps become reality.

(December 29, 1961)

XVIII

Science and the Arts of Man

WHEN QUESTIONS ARE ASKEW, answers can be nothing but askew except by accident. It may be that science can no longer ask the questions essential for man's continued ascent from the cave. Perhaps those questions can now emerge only from that area of non-science that may be called the arts of man.

While all inter-relationships are complex, the inter-relationship between science and culture has become especially so. Between science and culture is a widening gap of incomprehension more frequently widened than bridged by experts and specialists.

Man's instrumentation and mechanical extensions are capable of supplying all sorts of answers; but these answers, of themselves, add little to the reservoir of wisdom. Perhaps wisdom is more intimately related to questions than to answers. The misdirection of today's science — with its promise and threat so coupled that the removal of threat could shatter promise — stems from its ineptitude, its inability to ask those significant questions upon which the future of mankind depends.

Questions are seeds, and answers take their shapes and values from questions. For many reasons the seed may not germinate, and the question may, for many reasons, remain unanswered; but the seeds of inquiry continue to be the determining factors which shape a society through its aspirations.

Through the many ages of Man on Earth this applies to individuals as well as to nations.

If the most important question of the day is: "What's for dessert?" the answer is easily available at every meal. In a dessert-governed society one lives in anticipation of the dessert, even when, for various reasons, there may be no dessert.

If the dominant question of government is: "What of the enemy?" major goals can then be determined for the nation — not by its own aspirations, but by the enemy. Love of country can then be measured by intensity of hatred for the enemy.

If the consuming question of our age is: "How soon can we land on the moon?" we then become dominated by our satellite, and our planet is reduced to a launching-platform for our aspirations.

For an individual to ask questions that are essential to him and his immediate environment means that he must think; and the process of thinking automatically places him in opposition to status quo, which cannot tolerate basic questions from the individual. Such questions endanger the acquiescence and over-contentment that status quo constantly seeks to engender and maintain. The disposition of status quo is not to accept questions but to offer answers. An accumulation of answers, especially to non-basic questions, not only reinforces status quo but inevitably renders an already acquiescent society even more rigidly restrictive toward the individual. This sort of progression toward immobility of the individual seems valid throughout all structures of society from families to governments. It is precisely such rigidity, resulting from the instant availability of quick answers even before questions have fully been formed, that leaches all toughness and pliancy from the individual, and accelerates his subsequent fracture and mechanical reduction into the acquiescent mass.

For some individuals each day is mainly a new beginning; for others it is mainly proof that the prior day ended; for many it is simultaneously beginning and ending. It is the nature of simultaneity that meaning can be extracted only after values have been attributed to those unknown qualities that are common denominators to the various segments partaking of simultaneity.

In algebra — actually the reunion of broken parts, a mathematical word which stems from the Arabic for bonesetting — simultaneous equations define two or more equations that are satisfied and placed in balance by the same sets of values for the unknown quantities. If values cannot be established, the equations remain unsatisfied and unbalanced.

However, attempts to establish values, even if such attempts fail to satisfy the equation, can often in themselves be beneficial by eliminating areas from further barren consideration, thereby permitting the concentration of effort within areas of possible solution. The firm "no" is clearly more affirmative than the tentative "yes."

When attempts are not made, values for the equation can be found only by accident. The achievement of balance should scarcely be left to accident.

The mere elimination of areas from further consideration can hardly be sufficient if, in the process of elimination, so much effort is expended that little energy remains for the search for possible solution within the remaining areas. The elimination process itself can be permitted to become so exhaustive that not enough energy remains for the recognition of solution and the subsequent demonstration of proof.

Whether each day is a new beginning, a proof of yesterday's ending, or simultaneously beginning and ending, the search for solution — the asking of questions — is, of itself, a rebellion of the individual in search of reason and personal balance. Such rebellion may be suspect by the reinforcers of status quo; but it remains the basic attribute of man's creativity because the seeds of inquiry determine the nature of man's aspirations. Unfortunately, the nature of rebellion is such that it can become chiefly an eliminating process; a segmented peristalsis of one particular disorder that seems to be out of balance — it may actually be so — and then of another particular disorder in seeming unbalance. Such a search can become a random sort of thing, finding values only by accident — a tentative sort of fox-hunt where, in the absence of a live fox, a coyote-skin is dragged along the terrain by a retainer in order that the ritual of the hunt may be indulged in by the properly garbed and mounted. When the search for solutions becomes clothed in ritual, the ritual of rebellion nullifies rebellion; the ritual itself becomes the container and restrictor of the individual seeking personal balance. How can he discover even the nature of his personal rebellion when his energies are expended chiefly in ritual? when, at the end of a successful fox-hunt, all he has acquired is a long-dead coyote-skin?

Yet the fertile soil of non-science, of the arts of man wherein questions are generated for the emergence of man's comprehension of himself and his society, remains largely uncultivated throughout the world. Our ingenious mechanical devices and techniques for comprehension, for the nurturing and blending of people's aspirations, seem to expand our cultural wastelands.

The unit of man is the least common denominator of the arts of man. Despite segmentations and stratifications resulting from the power-centrifuge in which we seem to be spinning so much of the time, this unity and inseparability remains the least common denominator of the arts of man.

The arts of man may, at their best, be creative toward the individual when, from any starting-point, he achieves a universe; they may not be at all creative but only mimicry when, from every starting-point, he feels safe only when traveling the smoothed segments of the paths of others. However, unless corrupted by design, and except as they may be wasteful of his substance, the arts of man are not destructive toward the individual.

Science, however, can create or destroy; it can so obviously be simultaneously creative and destructive. Here, too, the nature of simultaneity is such that meaning can be extracted only after values have been attributed to unknown qualities, usually in retrospect. The abilities to attribute values to the unknown qualities of science do not reside essentially within the scientist because he is a scientist, but within the creative aspects of man — scientist and non-scientist — within the non-ritualized rebellion which is the basic attribute of man's creativity. In this context, after questions have been generated within non-science, science may then seek their answers.

Scientific answers emerge through measurability, through the brilliant use of dimensions. That which is measurable — in whatever form of measurement — becomes the proper subject of science in mathematics, physics, chemistry, biology, medicine — in all of science. When new measurements are added to a particular discipline it becomes more exact, more scientific; and new areas of inquiry are often exposed through such additional measurements. For science the least common denominator remains measurability and containment. That which is not measurable at the time of inquiry, even through the use of X-the-unknown, is rejected as not being within the proper scope of the current science, and hence not its responsibility.

Man is measurable as a statistic only when he is segmented because the segments are then measurable; and when the individual collaborates in his own reduction into a grouping of statistics, he becomes measurable. Whenever the individual permits himself to become compartmentalized, he becomes less than unity and less than man; it is then that he descends into the scope of science. However, if he retains his individuality and untamability by refusing to become enmassed, there is no available dimension by which he can be measured and contained. What dimension can be used to measure Socrates or Shakespeare, or your grandfather's grandfather? There is no dimension for the statically dead, much less for the dynamically living. Dimensionality presupposes a point of reference that will remain static for the fraction of time needed to affix whatever measure is attempted. The attempt to measure man, the attempt itself, alters man; this happens not only because man cannot be made static long enough for the application of measurement — for who would make him static? — but essentially because non-static man is the only measurer of his constantly changing self.

Retaining his individual immeasurability, man cannot be the responsibility of science.

Is he then the responsibility of non-science, of the arts of man?

He cannot be solely the responsibility of non-science because science simply cannot be made to vanish from man's arsenal of abilities. Even should the physical arsenal of the products of his abilities be made to vanish, man retains a measure of recall and skill through which the physical arsenal could be reconstituted. The recall and skill are part of man's total environment.

Is it possible for man to become the joint responsibility of science and non-science? Could a blending of two such dissimilar forces generate the harmonious sharing of responsibility for the future of mankind? Can science, whose least common denominator remains measurability, be joined with non-science, whose least common denominator remains man's immeasurability? Or will the rising antagonisms surging between science and non-science, between mass-man and individual-man, generate increasing chaos across the entire body of mankind?

This question is a point of pivot of our time.

Once upon a time there was deep philosophy, which literally means the love of wisdom, throughout much of science which was then, most certainly, a liberating concept. Many of its applications, refined through technology, have released mankind from the brutalization of animal-toil and paralyzing fears of the unknown. Science was then apolitical and amoral, and it cherished its universality. Its historic role had been a continuous attempt to seek order from chaos, from the confused state of primordial matter that existed prior to the extraction of knowledgeable orderly forms. But science seems to have lost its love of wisdom.

Scientific order, of itself, does not eliminate the possibility of new and more brutish chaos being generated from its findings by scientist and non-scientist. When science became political it simultaneously became immoral. When it permitted its inherent universality to become contained, to be restricted, it could no longer accept guidance or verify its bearings from a love of wisdom. The monumental order abstracted by the pre-atomic age scientists was so hastily transformed by political expediency, in which scientists certainly participated, into the mushrooming explosion. The explosion itself was rejected by science as not being its responsibility — and again, perhaps correctly.

The contributions of science to mankind always far outweighed its disturbances of mankind until near the middle of this century when, becoming political, it rejected the love of wisdom. Throughout history science always sustained its quiet rebellion against ignorance, prejudice and containment. It was an international pursuit of knowledge by individuals cherishing their individuality, searching to expose the unknown. Scientists never formed a quiet monastic brotherhood; there were great personal antagonisms, prejudices and conflicts among them; but science itself was never in opposition to man. Obviously, the successful militarization of science depended upon the submission of the individual scientist to a higher authority exerting the capital power of expediency. For the scientist, the highest authority had heretofore been science. Yet he submitted. With his submission began the torsion of science. Mankind now seems to proceed only with the aid of the technological crutch.

How can love of wisdom be restricted to man-made boundaries and contained within geographic segments? At tempts at such restrictions and segmentations debase science and degrade scientists.

Many scientists have recently become concerned with the widening gap between unavoidable specialization of science and the imperative need for comprehension between science and non-science, science and culture. This is a just, though late, concern.

If the gap between science and the arts of man cannot be bridged, it seems unavoidable for man to become increasingly enmassed, increasingly dimensioned and restricted. Science, alone, appears to be incapable of leading or herding mankind onto any alternative path. Through its devices, it can assure mankind only of the statistical possibility of total erasure; it cannot guarantee any sort of survival. It can offer new dimensions, new measurements and new disciplines; but basic to all that science can offer is an increased attempt at the measurability of man. Even if unsuccessful, the response to such attempts can be nothing less than increased conformity. The basic immeasurability of the individual resisting enmassment is an uncomfortable concept for science, which thrives on measurability, to contemplate.

If the gap between science and non-science is not bridged science, with its inexorable actualities and promises, will predominate over the arts of man. These inexorabilities of science offer the individual physical abundance and material ease not only in terms of gadgetry but throughout all aspects of mechanical daily living; and they offer emerging nations and peoples the material abundance which has become the physical evidence of independence. Because science can embrace individuals and peoples without requiring from them any comprehension of science, its spread can be rapid and relentless. None of this is available in the arts of man, which require deep individual comprehension for their promises to become actualities. The arts of man cannot simultaneously offer promise and threat.

In order to continue to function in science, the individual scientist must constantly deepen his specialty. In each specialty a mountain-barrage of answers continues to rise before the scientist — occasionally as a challenge, and often as a barrier — and he must be at least aware of the presence of answers, and the further deepening of his specialty. The constant deepening of areas to measurability and the exposure of new areas to measurability increase his compartmentalization because his ability and opportunity to contribute to science are usually related to his own segmentation. The non-specialist in science finds himself orphaned. The resultant torsion of the confined specialist presages conformity, or ritualized rebellion, either of which increases his enmassment and depletes his value as an individual, a total human being.

There is a barbarism to specialization, an inevitable sort of cannibalism, of segments consuming themselves. The great man-spawned computers and devices increase this cannibalistic self-consumption because man's mechanical extensions stem from attempts to dimension man by first segmenting him into units of measurability. How can the sum of segments, regardless of volume, be transmuted into the wholeness of man's immeasurability?

It is precisely such segmentation that makes the scientist himself increasingly measurable in terms of his utility; increasingly enmassed, dimensioned, and restricted. This measurability accelerates the permeability of science throughout mankind and the emergence of mass-man. It would seem that the scientist is becoming the precursor of mass-man.

Individual-man, even in science, cannot seek guidance from science, which seeks to absorb him. Should the arts of man become dimensioned, the statistical reduction of the individual into the mass for all of his remaining time seems inevitable. By resisting segmentation, the arts of man retain immeasurability and individual-man may then survive. Guidance for survival here cannot come from science, but only, it would seem, from the arts of man.

Bereft of philosophy, of the love of wisdom, it would seem that the basic questions of science are now askew. How could their answers be anything but askew?

Realization of this skewness generates such bewilderment among those scientists who wish to reject their isolation that many descend deeper into the caves of specialization carved out of man's totality, from whence they flash intermittent pencil-thin lights in the hope salvation may be guided to them.

If the scientist attempts an expansion into the arts of man he frequently finds himself restricted by his desire for precise measurements and verifiable facts, by his almost unavoidable discipline-of-segmentation — as though paintings could be evaluated through the Angstrom Units of wavelength of the colors on the canvas. His studied discipline encourages the scientist to approach the arts of man on a project-basis and he may quickly know far more about paints than the painter whose primary involvment is not with segments of color, but with a unit of his creativity.

In science, a unit of creativity is fixed throughout space and time. Unless it is replaced throughout the universe, two-plus-two remains four throughout the universe. In science a unit has no individual meaning; it can be used as a foundation upon which to build all sorts of structures; but the unit itself remains unchanged. If found lacking in value as a result of new scientific knowledge, it is totally replaced by another unit. But the unit of science has no growth-factor; it is fixed unless replaced. When it is replaced it assumes only historical interest, and can no longer be used as a foundation. A science unit is, for example, the multiplication table — of enormous value and enormous rigidity.

If there is a unit of creativity, it cannot be fixed; it must have individual meaning and a fluid universality. Each individual partaking of this unit of creativity can abstract meaning only if he contributes something of himself, thereby becoming enriched.

Non-science, the undimensioned and unlimited creativity of man, can recognize, accept, and cherish man's totality. To remove barriers so that creativity and its comprehension can flow freely among peoples, to breathe life into data-fragments so that they, their concepts, and their seeds become part of the growth and dignity of the individual and his society is the everlasting wonder of man's creativity.

Instrumentation for man's comprehension of himself and his ecology — his inter-relationship with his total environment — cannot come from science because dimensions beget dimensions. While science possesses great fertilizing value for mankind's growth — although so frequently only through the composting of the individual — many of its seeds and expectations do not belong to it; they still belong to those immeasurable aspirations that remain the arts of man.

But these arts also seem to be askew. Since the atomic age began they have produced so little of value and guidance for mankind. How else to account for the mushrooming emergence of mass-culture to pacify mass-man? For the acceptance of mass-threat as a way of life? For the social and economic security of the scientist and the insecurity of the individual seeking expression in his creativity? For the cultural wastelands made increasingly arid by those creative people who collaborate in their own impotence by accelerating the cultural pacification of mass-man? How else to account for the scarcity and bare survival of those oases in the wastelands from which mankind can draw cultural nourishment?

Is it because novelists, sculptors, painters, formal philosophers, critics, seem to be guided by segmentation-principles instead of a love of wisdom? Unrelated to reality they, too, seem to be groping in caves, planting no seeds, harvesting only what is carried to them by the erratic gusts of their own indecisions and uncertainties. Is it because they accept guidance from the segmentation-principles of science, and find themselves best able to function creatively only when some external measurements restrain them? Restraint is certainly organic to creativity; but it would seem that here the restraint needs to be an internal holding-back of forces rather than an external dimensionality which sets boundaries.

It is entirely possible that the segmentation-principles governing science will force it to become increasingly dimensioned, restrictive, and finally static. Despite moon-shots, science can impose upon mankind a decaying immobility where the individual can move only as the mass moves. Can the arts of man survive such immobility? It hardly seems likely.

The arts of man, it would seem, can survive through non-science's becoming so staunchly resolute in the practice of its arts and the cherishing of its freedom from segmentation that the arts of man will then be able to generate those basic seeds of inquiry which determine the shape of society. The immense ability of science to acquire answers can then be given the guidance needed.

It would be exhilarating indeed if men of science were also men of culture — as, at the time when their roots were deep in the love of wisdom, they surely were. But today's science, based as it is upon the segmentation of the individual, is on the path toward barbarism. It is not unusual for a scientist to seek and find mathematics in Bach; but seldom does he seek Bach in mathematics.

Can men of culture then become men of science?

Since each discipline requires a full measure of time and devotion in order to survive in a complex society, this would seem unlikely; and a mere casual awareness of the complexity science has become could be dangerous.

Science and non-science in organic union, not in mechanical mixture and mere acceptance, may enable man to fulfill his potentialities by presenting him with a new concept and understanding of his ecology — presently altered beyond

recall and return to its prior state, but perhaps not beyond
redemption and deliverance from its prior bondage.

The segmentations of science are dangerous to mankind;
so, too, are the segmentations of non-science, of which there
are many.

Can these two dissimilar forces simultaneously generate
the harmonious sharing of responsibility for the future of
mankind?

This question will certainly determine man's direction
and his future. Here again, the nature of simultaneity —
especially as it refers to the uneasy symbiosis, the uncomfortable co-existence of science and non-science — is such
that purpose can be abstracted only after values have been
attributed to those qualities of science and non-science whose
effects upon the future of mankind remain unknown.

The ability to attribute values to the unknown qualities
of this torsioned inter-relationship reside within the creative
aspects of man — scientist and non-scientist. They do not
reside in his mechanical extensions, whether these are in
technology or in cultural mimicry, but only within the non-
ritualized rebellion which is the basic seed of individual-
man's creativity.

(March 23, 1962)

Postscript

Postscript

WHAT IS MAN FOR?

Whether asked in anger or anguish, in frustration or defiance, in humility or arrogance or despair, what man is for remains a question of both cosmic and intimate significance to the individuals of each successive generation of Man on Earth.

Along the dim trails that lead to knowledge and wisdom each traveler must verify his own bearings and identify for himself the dangers that hinder or obstruct his passage. The good wishes of others for his safe emergence and their good intent toward generating ease of passage do not, of themselves, fill chasms, remove boulders, lay ghosts, or quiet the fears of the actual and the unknown. Good wishes and good intentions cannot identify bearings.

While it is true that today's science has not simplified our lives but burdened us with a complexity analogous to that which would result from the addition of another letter to our alphabet, the inescapable and exhilarating fact is that we are here, now, on our host, the Earth. There is no turning back for a new genesis.

Certainly man is more than a consumptive-unit, more than a biologic organism charged only with his own continuance, and more than a generator of obliterative threat.

But how much more?

Man is here. What is he for?

Each must seek his own answer.

The search could of itself lead to a design-theory for Man on Earth.

(July 4, 1962)

Lewis and Clark College - Watzek Library
HM101 .C52   wmain
Charter, S P/Man on earth; a prel

3 5209 00419 0928